A Dressed Up Mess

By Allie West

A Dressed Up Mess by Allie West

Books may be purchased by contacting the publisher and author at: www.alliewest.com or info@alliewest.com

Editor: Attiyya Atkins, A+ Editing & Content Creation

ISBN: 978-1-64136-993-0

Printed in USA

Contents

Dedication

This book is dedicated to my father, my rock, Tommy Lee Hunt Sr., who transitioned on November 21, 2014. I know you watch over me from the other side and send me ladybugs to let me know you are still with me. Love transcends death.

To Danny "Disco Dan" Jackson, who unknowingly introduced me to a different caliber of men. He taught me to embrace everything about my womanhood, especially the intimate sensual side. He stood by as I weathered some of life's storms. When I told him about the book and asked what he wanted his name to be, he said "Danny" – I want everyone to know you're talking about me. He called me periodically to say, "Where's the book, I want my signed copy first." Unfortunately, my dear friend transitioned on April 25, 2018. I miss you my friend!

A Dressed Up Mess

Preface

You must look beyond the lace front wig, the flawless makeup, the French-manicured nails, and pedicured feet. Scroll past the name-brand clothing and designer heels. I'm Allie West. I'm colorful, charismatic, and funny. I'm well-educated, well-dressed, and well-poised. The proudest peacock, all dressed up as if I don't have a care in the world. But, on the inside, I am a mess, I just don't know how the world doesn't see it. On the surface you see me – all dressed up – minus the internal chaos. I am fragile. I am a mess! How did I end up here? Better question, how do I get out?

"Bitch, I will leave you here stranded!"

"I hate you and your kids! I hate dark-skin women!"

"I hate I came and got you and moved you here."

"I'm putting you on a thirty-day notice, try not to speak to me in during that time and I'll do the same."

"You're a Goddamn fuck up!"

These words play in my head as I lay *here. Here.* Where is here you may wonder? Here is home, literally back home at my parent's house in Tulsa, Oklahoma, a place I'd vowed never to come back to. Too many bad memories *here*! But here I am with everything I own in a twenty-six foot Penske truck, my car on a tow dolly parked in an empty lot up the street, my two babies are snuggled up in bed with me as I replay the nightmare of Austin and our life in Phoenix.

I am exhausted, but I can't sleep. Its cold in here, I'm ashamed. I'm guilty. I'm hurt. I'm mad and I am wounded! How do I overcome this setback? *I hate Tulsa! Fuck!* I want to cry, but I can't – I can't disturb my children. I can only imagine what they are thinking about me. Damn, here I am starting over again after living the dream life in Atlanta and giving it all up for love. This shit is crazy! I hope no one asks me why I moved back, I don't know myself. Maybe I should have kept driving to Atlanta. My mind is on high-speed internet and my body is on dial-up. I need some rest; I toss and turn for what seems hours. I finally drift off to sleep.

How Did I End Up Here?

In this Texas heat, 111 degrees feels like 130. It's August and the heat waves bounce to create a mirage off the concrete highway. Beads of sweat are dripping from our faces. Timothy and Cicely are frustrated and arguing. I am really trying to hold it together, but this was a trip from hell from the start.

Frustrated, I took the long route from Phoenix to avoid the steep, curvy mountains of Flagstaff, Arizona. Driving a moving truck at 7,000 feet altitudes with no guardrails made me nervous. The thought of us plunging to our deaths over the mountains made me take the longer, more scenic route. Seven more hours to be exact. Dang, what's seventeen plus seven? A twenty-four-hour drive to the last place I want to be on Earth. Well, the last place aside from Phoenix.

It's 2:09 a.m. I pull the twenty-six-foot Penske truck into Tulsa, Oklahoma. This journey is a nightmare that I anxiously want to end. I am exhausted and want to get to my parents' house and lay down in a comfortable bed.

Everything I own is in this truck and some of Austin's stuff too. My car is still secure, thank God. My babies, Cicely and Timothy, are sound asleep. I know they're uncomfortable in this tiny cab. If anyone had asked if I'd ever move back home, the answer would have been a firm, unequivocal "Hell Naw!" However, this is exactly what I'm doing, moving back to my childhood home.

Construction is everywhere, and all these detours have me confused. I came in on Interstate 40, but now I'm on I-244. I've lost my sense of direction. Oh, thank goodness, here's the Tisdale exit and North Cincinnati Avenue is just ahead. In ten minutes, I can turn this big, loud ass, gas-guzzling truck off and place my feet on solid ground. If I was driving from Atlanta, I could have done it blindfolded, but not this excursion. This is a hard, emotionally charged, and drama-filled trip. I'm sleepy, hungry, and confused, but most of all hurt.

How did I miss that this motherfucker is so crazy, or did I just ignore the signs, foolishly believing that love conquers all bullshit?

This truck is loud and wide. I hope I don't wake up any of the neighbors, especially the nosey ones. I don't feel like explaining why I am here to anybody. I pull up along the curbside across the street from my parent's house in front of two empty houses. The truck's tow dolly extends and blocks several driveway so, I maneuver into the vacant lot just up the street.

"Cecily, Timothy wake up, we're here!" They don't budge. "Hey, do y'all hear me? I said wake up! Grab what you need for now, and we will figure things out in the morning."

Still sleepy, they manage to grab their essentials, and we walk with our arms interlocked to my parents' house. My dad is standing in the front door with the porch light on.

"Hey, daddy."

"Hey, grandpa," Timothy and Cecily chimed in unison.

"Hey, are y'all hungry?"

"Yes." We walk in the house. My mother is laying in the den on the couch. "Y'all made it?" she asks.

"Yes, finally," I said.

"Get you something to eat, your daddy cooked. We've been waiting for y'all to get here. We can't sleep knowing y'all were on the road."

"Trust, we've been ready to be here," I said.

"I know y'all are tired, that was a long trip. You're a brave young lady, always have been," she said proudly.

We quickly ate and found places to lie down. Tired as I was, I couldn't settle down. I'm wired from the trip and now trying to fall asleep in my brother's room, all the old feelings and experiences about Tulsa come rushing back. Both of my brothers were murdered – their cases are still unsolved. Still in shock at life's turns, I brush my teeth, wash my face, peel my clothes off and crawl into bed.

This house is freezing, my mother has the Thermostat set to Arctic blast. If I didn't know any better, I would think I was in Alaska. The temperature is in stark contrast to the triple-digit temperatures that we traveled through in Arizona and Texas. I bundle up in the heavy comforters. I'm lying in the stillness of the night, thinking, *how did I get here?* My mind wanders back to the trip we just endured.

"Mom, please just keep going, let's bypass Tulsa and go back to Atlanta...You'll find a job. We can stay with Aunt Renee until we find a place to live. Please, mom, please!"

I completely understand that Cicely doesn't want to live in Tulsa, I don't either. I can't return to Atlanta – not like this, jobless, homeless, loveless, and much less of who I was before. Damn, I just left Atlanta three months ago. We move a lot, but this is a record, even for us – we've lived in three states this year. A few months ago, my life was stable. What happened?

His Name is Austin

Austin Phillips happened. I left Atlanta in May 2010, following who I thought was the love of my life to Phoenix. I remember the first time I saw my brother Donald's friend, Austin. He came to one of the many house parties that my siblings hosted. Now keep in mind, I am the baby of ten combined children, obviously, they saved the best for last. I was supposed to be in my room during the party, but the house was packed with teenagers and young adults. I wasn't missing anything, plus, I loved to dance. I spotted him sitting on the couch in the den. He was fine, and I fell in love at first sight.

Most of the night, he sat and people watched, but George Clinton will bring even the most reserved homebody to the floor. When "Atomic Dog" glared from the loudspeakers, Austin popped up and jammed to "Why must I feel like that, why must I chase the cat, the dog in me, nothing but the dog in me. Bow-wow-wow-yippie-yo-yippie-yeah, bow-wow-yippie-yo-yippie-yeah." I could not resist approaching Austin when the GAP Band crooned

"Outstanding,"…. "You want to dance? I'm Donald's sister, Allison."

"Sure," we grooved to Charlie's silky voice. "You blow my mind baby, I'm so alive with you baby. Austin joined in "you light my fire; I feel alive with you baby. You blow my mind, I'm satisfied."

After that party, Austin started to come around a lot more, whether playing dominoes, spades or sitting in the den watching BET, he was a regular fixture around our house. Austin was different from Donald's other loud, rambunctious, and mannish friends. He was quiet, gentle, and humble. I would always find a reason to talk to him. Funny, I never told him that I had a crush on him.

The years passed, and Donald and Austin graduated from high school. Austin moved to Phoenix, and I didn't see him again until six years later when I was nineteen. I was practically grown by my account, and home from college. He stopped by to visit Donald. I remember that visit vividly, he asked Donald to visit Phoenix and claimed he could get him a job with the airlines if he moved there. I wish Donald would have moved; he was murdered the next year.

12

That visit, I finally told Austin that I had a crush on him since we'd met. "I had a crush on you too Allison, but you're Donald's little sister, so you were off limits."

"I'm not little anymore," I teased.

"I see you aren't, you're a beautiful young lady, but out of respect for my homeboy I can't, as bad as I want to."

I wouldn't see Austin again for many years. Once Donald died, he stopped visiting, but he did call my parents periodically to check on them. Mom would tell me, "Austin, called and asked about you."

I would respond, "Really, tell him I said hi when you talk to him again."

"He left his number for you."

"Ok, I'll reach out to him."

We'd keep contact for a short while and then lose touch again. I moved to Atlanta when I was twenty-five. Over the next several years, we sporadically keep in contact. Most of the time, it was over the phone and occasionally face-to-face. We fell out in 2006 after the bastard had the nerve to tell me – after we'd slept together, that he was still in love with his ex-wife. The last I'd heard is that he was in prison for distributing exotic drugs.

Fast forward two and a half years, and I'm sitting here alone at home on New Year's Eve. I'm not interested in going out tonight, and I don't want to go to church. I guess I'll watch some television. Dang, where did I sit my phone and who's calling me?

"Hello."

"Hey Allison, its Austin Phillips, how are you?"

I'm silent. I am shocked to hear from him.

"Hello, are you there?"

I know my momma gave him my number.

"Hey, Austin," I manage to say.

"I know that you are probably shocked to hear from me and I can understand why," he says nonchalantly.

I don't know how to feel. I mean I am glad to hear his voice. This isn't a collect call, so apparently, he's out of prison, but I'm still salty about the bullshit he pulled the last time we were together.

On the flip side, I have a soft spot for Austin. No matter how many years between us – every time I hear his voice, I revert to the young girl that's been crushing on him since the day we met. I'm conflicted.

"It's good to hear your voice."

"Allison, if you'll just listen for a moment, I have some things I've been waiting to say to you for a long time. First, I apologize for how things ended with us the last time we were together, you didn't deserve that. It has bothered me for years that I did that to you. I was in a difficult place in my life I'd just gotten a divorce that I didn't want, but she did. I was still in love with her, so I shouldn't have pulled you into that. I'm also sorry for missing Donald's funeral, he was one of my best friends, and I just couldn't see him like that. I wanted to remember him the way he was the last time I saw him, laughing and joking. I know it hurt your mom, dad, and you that I wasn't there, but I had to deal with it the best way I could."

Five hours later and we were still talking. "Now look Austin, I've got to get off this phone," I say hurriedly.

"I know. Allison, it feels so good to be talking to you. Thank you, my Queen, for hearing me out and bringing in the New Year with me."

"Happy 2009, Austin, good night."

"Good night, Allison, you still have a beautiful spirit."

For the next several months Austin and I spend countless hours on the phone talking, texting, and sending pictures. He needed a friend, and that was all that I could offer him after my engagement to Jamal fell apart. I am focused on my kids and my career.

Meanwhile, Austin was getting adjusted to life after prison. He had given power of attorney to his niece Skye to manage his affairs while he was away. She had access to $100,000, two homes, multiple credit cards, a Benz, and the fleet of luxury vehicles that belonged to his transportation company. Three years later – he was no longer living a life of luxury.

Austin called me early one morning, "Hey Allison, what's up girl? What's going on in the A?"

"What's up Austin? You sound sad, are you alright?"

"Still adjusting and still uncovering details of how much my family really stole from me while I was on "vacation," so far I've found out about $52,000 that they just fucked off. I've lost both my homes, my Benz and now my credit is smashed. The only thing I have left is one limo. At least I can work..."

Austin goes on.

"I hate working for Antonio's ass, but it is what it is. It's hard to stay in this house with Skye knowing she stole from me, but I have to do what I have to do to rebuild. I'm a businessman I know how to make money."

"Legally, right?" We're laughing, but I'm serious.

"Yes, legally. I made most of my money legally before I got greedy, trust me, I ain't ever going back to prison."

"Good," I chime in.

"Baby, I've got to have to take this call, I'll call you back. I love you." Did Austin just call me baby and say he loves me? Oh, I am not ready for this, it's too soon. I feel like a girl with a high school crush, but I can't repeat those words back to him. Anyway, our situation is the same, he's in Phoenix, and I'm in Atlanta, this has been our story for over a dozen years.

Happily Ever After, Here We Come

Our relationship is changing. Austin calls me all day long to know where I am, what I am doing and who I'm doing it with.

"I can't get you off my mind Allison, I think about you and the kids every day. I want to come to Atlanta for a visit, so I can check it out. The A may be a good spot to rebuild Phillips' Signature Transportation Services."

"You should, I think you'll like it here," I say eagerly. Honestly, he stays on my mind too. I have no intentions of falling for him, but I think it's too late. Cicely and Timothy notice the changes in me and ask me questions like I am their child.

"Mom, who are you on the phone with, all the time?"

"...Yeah mom, you are always smiling and excited. We can hear him singing to you through the phone, you know."

I let them talk to Austin. "He seems pretty cool, are

we going to meet him? "He's coming for a visit to meet you guys and check out Atlanta."

It's April 30 and Austin's flight gets in at 10:00 p.m. Good, I'm early, plenty of time to meet him inside. I know airport security is only going to let me get so far. I am so freaking excited, I'm about to see my baby! I spot Austin as he exits the escalator. He sees me too; I can tell by the big grin spreading across his face as he rushes over to hug me.

"Welcome to the ATL, baby," I say full of joy.

"Thank you, baby, I am glad to be here." He grabs his luggage, and we head to the house. On the ride home, we kiss at every red light.

"We're here, welcome to our home, Cicely and Timothy are asleep you'll have to meet them tomorrow."

"I wish I would have caught an earlier flight. I am looking forward to meeting them. Thank you for having me in your home, it means a lot Allison."

"Let me give you a quick tour. This is the guest room where you'll be staying."

Austin sat his bags down, and we continued the tour. This is my bedroom, Austin grabs me around the waist, pulling me closer to him. We kiss passionately. The sexual tension overtakes us, and we make love in the middle the floor. It feels good to lay here in his arms without complications of ex-wives or ex-fiancées. Austin grabs his bags, and we take a long shower together. We fell asleep in each other's arms.

Time flew by, Austin leaves for Phoenix today. We're both walking around here like lovesick puppies. There is no denying that we are in love. The issue is, what are we going to do? Austin is rebuilding, and I am focused on the kids and my career. I can't move, my career is going well. I'm in graduate school, and Cicely is graduating high school in a year. I've applied to become a consultant to earn extra money, so my roots are firm in Atlanta. Austin has more flexibility, he can build his company here. We ponder over what to do over the next few months.

We're on the phone making final plans for his upcoming visit, and then, "Baby, I think someone just stole my car, I'm outside, and it's not where I parked it. Let me call you right back," Austin says.

I'm in the grocery store when he calls back.

"Baby, you won't believe this shit, I just got off the phone with the bank, Skye's ass been lying to me, she did not pay my car off. My car was repossessed. I've been calling her, and her ass won't answer her phone. I don't know how much more or this I can take. I've got to get out of here before I snap. I'm going to buy a plane ticket with what I've saved up. I can't take this anymore."

With love or ulterior motives as his guide, Austin moves to Atlanta with no car, no job, no money and a felony record. I know this is a recipe for disaster. We're sitting on the bed talking, and he blurts out, "Baby let's get married. I love you. I don't want to be without you and the kids ever again! Will you do me the honor of being my wife?" I'm thinking, I can't say no, I'm finally going to get married, this is what I've always wanted.

"Yes, Austin, yes, I'll marry you," I say. I am sure you are thinking, girl, you are stupid, you should run like Forrest Gump! Run, girl, run!

Cupid knocked me out, I am a love-sick fool. I couldn't see Austin's bad juju even if it was painted across my face. I rationalize my stupidity with dumb shit, like, love conquers all, plus we've got a long history. That's got to account for something. With love, we can do this. Happily ever after, here we come.

In a family meeting, I announce to Cicely and Timothy, "There is a new sheriff in town, and you guys are going to have to get in line, don't give me any shit." They both look at me as if my head is spinning. The transition to Atlanta is a motherfucker. Austin lived a ballers life before his downfall. He owned a million-dollar home, luxury cars, and expensive clothes and accessories. Versace, Cartier and Rolex were a few of his favorite brands. His credit was good, and he had access to cash. He'd been on his own since he was nineteen and never depended on anyone.
Now, he can't find a job and is frustrated that he can't provide for our family. I am carrying the weight of the relationship on my $50,000 a year salary.

Through it all, I am in love with him. I love him past his flaws, and I believe that my love can heal his pain. And he was brutally broken, I wanted him so bad that I missed all the warning signs. One time, I forgot to call Austin to let him know about a meeting that ran late:

"Hey, baby, what's up?"

"Where are you?"

"I'm leaving work, I forgot about this meeting today, it just ended."

"Call me from your office," he demanded.

"Baby, I'm getting in the car, everyone is leaving, and the building is about to close."

"Allie, call me from your office phone."

"Why?" I'm confused.

"Just do it," he says forcefully.

"Okay, let me see if the door is still unlocked."

"Talk to me while you go back into the building."

I pass a couple of colleagues who ask if I am ok.

I lied. "I'm fine, I forgot something," I told them.

"I'm in my office now." I pick up the phone to call Austin then realize I can't. "Austin, I can't dial long distance from my office phone."

"Okay baby, I'll see you when you get home, drive safe." I thought that was odd, but I let it go.

Dinner is ready most evenings when I get home, and he keeps the house immaculate. It is his way of contributing. The stress of not working is driving Austin crazy. Our sex life is strained, Austin cums before I can barely get wet. Time is passing and nothing is happening for Austin.

"I can hardly believe you've been here eight months," I say.

"Allie, I've got to get back to Phoenix, I'm dying here, and I need to rebuild, and I can't do it in Atlanta." I am relieved that he is leaving, but I'll miss him.

Change of Plans

The plan is for Austin to return to Phoenix to establish his business. We'll join him after Cicely graduates, enrolls in college, and I finish grad school. We will be in a better financial position. In the interim, we are alternating monthly visits. Now that Austin is back in Phoenix the plan is in action. He uses one of Antonio's cars until he purchases his own. Things are shifting, and Austin is much happier. He loves to work, and he loves money, so he's working hard. Absence does make the heart grow fonder – we're on the phone every day, talking, texting, sending pictures and having phone sex. Austin serenades me with Charlie Wilson when he calls. Today I answered to his silky voice singing, "Hey girl, how you doing? My name is Austin, last name Phillips. I was wondering if I could take you out, show you a good time, invite you to my house. Here is my number, girl you can call me. And don't forget it baby, the name is Austin…"

I am grinning from ear to ear. "You know you can sing, I love it when you sing to me."

"I'll be singing to you the rest of my life baby."
Austin is such a romantic.

December is here, and Austin flies in today. He
showers me with expensive gifts – perfume, shades and
Cartier eyewear. He gives me money to buy Christmas gifts
for the kids. This is the perfect visit. He is more kind and
gentle than he was before he left. Here is the Austin I
remembered from years before. I can get used to this. This
time taking him to the airport and saying goodbye is hard. I
don't want to leave Austin, and he wants to stay. I won't let
him see me cry, I'll cry when I pull off.

New Year, New Journey

I just touched down in Phoenix. Man, I haven't been here since 2007. There's a lot of tension between Austin and his cousin Skye, and I feel a little uncomfortable being in the apartment. However, she is cordial to me. While Austin works, I complete schoolwork and catch up with friends. I'm glad Austin is off the next two days.

"What do you want to do, baby?" "I'm flexible, surprise me."

"I want to show you the good life, Allie. I want you to experience Phoenix like you've never have before. This weekend is all about you, we're balling out baby!"

We spend the weekend at the Wild Horse Bend Resort in Ahwatukee. It's beautiful here and were enjoying the serenity of the resort. Our view of the desert is amazing! I can't believe I'm watching wild horses galloping across the desert plains from our balcony. This is living, and I love it.

"Baby, we're starting the day with a shopping spree, then I'm going to take you to one of my favorite restaurants and then we'll join some friends for a rooftop birthday party. Tomorrow's agenda – site-seeing."

The scenic view of the large cactuses against the mountain backdrops are picturesque. After the busy day, I'm pooped, I just want to spend the evening relaxing in our room. I have an early flight, so I get my bags together to make sure I don't leave anything. I'm searching my purse for my buddy pass that Austin's friend gave me, but it isn't in here. I look all over the room and can't find it. We inquire with the front desk in hopes that someone may have turned it in. No one. Eventually, he calls his friend to tell him the pass is lost. That phone call revealed a different side of Austin.

"I can't believe you lost the fucking pass, do you know how this makes me look to Steve?"

"You act like I lost it on purpose…," I said dumb founded.

"I should leave your ass here and let you find your own goddamn ride to the airport."

I try to get him to relax, but it seems to irritate him. The pass is gone. It's never returning, so Austin has to purchase my ticket back to Atlanta. He starts cursing me out again,

"BITCH!," with a vile emphasis and rage. "I will leave you here, you figure out how to get to the airport and back to Atlanta, and when you get back, don't call me either," he grabs his car keys off the nightstand and heads for the door. I'm perplexed, "Austin, Austin, are you really going to leave me here stranded? Really baby, are you serious?" He glances back at me and grabs the door handle and leaves. I'm sitting on the bed, hurt and confused.

OK, Allison, what are you going to do? I feel flushed, and my eyes are burning from holding back the tears. I pick up my cell phone to call my friend D to see if he will take me to the airport. I did not want to explain to him how my Mr. Wonderful cursed me out and left me stranded at the resort. I take a deep breath and scroll to find D's number. I am about to press call when I hear a knock on the door. I set the phone down, stand up, wipe my eyes and fix my hair. I walk over to the door, "Who is it?"

"It's me, baby, open the door." Austin walks in, "I couldn't do it, I couldn't leave you, especially when I looked in your eyes and you said baby, are you going to really leave me here? You looked so sad. I'm sorry baby. I don't want to hurt you." He grabs me, hugs me, and starts kissing me. I am mad and want to slap the taste out of his mouth. But to keep the peace, I follow along. In bed, he holds me tight all night. I'm laying here thinking, what the hell just happened. I finally drift off to sleep.

Damn, he's already up, I hoped to get up before him. I quickly shower and get dressed. I don't want to be late arriving to the airport. I am not in the mood for any bullshit, I'm quiet, I don't have a damn thing to say to him. Still, Mr. Chatterbox tries to make small talk.

"Do you want breakfast?"

"No," I say plainly.

We ride in silence the remainder of the drive. When we arrive at the airport, I am ready to purchase my one-way ticket to Atlanta. I'm getting out of the car, but Austin stops me.

"Wait here, I'll be back. When he returns his mood is a little lighter than before. He opens my car door and introduces me to a guy who grabs my luggage from the trunk. "My friend will take care of you." The guy checks my bags, and Austin walks me into the airport. It is time for me to head to the gate. We hug hap heartedly, and he kisses me gently on the lips. "Cheer up, everything is going to be ok, I love you. Have a safe flight baby and call me as soon as you land, we're good." I give a forced grin and turn to walk towards the security checkpoint. "Hey, you don't love me?"

"I do…"

I just want to get on the plane and get home.

We skip our February visit because we're meeting in Las Vegas for my birthday in March. We're back on track, and I am excited about our trip. Unfortunately, I can't get a flight out this weekend because of Spring Break. Austin's flies to Atlanta the next week. We have a good visit, and it's getting harder to say goodbye. The long distance is wearing on us and the expenses of flying across the country every month is interfering with our savings plan. After this visit, Austin changes the plan. "I want you all to move to Phoenix this summer."

I protest, "We can visit every other month."

"No, that won't work, I hate leaving my family behind. I miss y'all. We go back and forth for weeks, I try to get him to see the benefit of waiting for another year, but he's stubborn. We plan to move once school gets out. The kids will go to Oklahoma so that we can get settled, and then they will fly to Phoenix just before school starts. The ball was in motion. I turn in my resignation letter to the surprise of everyone at work. I announce the plan to the kids. Timothy is delighted with the plan, Cicely is pissed. This starts a downward spiral. Cicely doesn't want to move away her senior year in high school, so now I am public enemy number one.

I attempt to get Cicely to buy into the idea of moving to Phoenix – but she isn't having it. The more that I try to make it seem like the best thing for our family, the more she rebels. She is angry with me, and she ensures that I know it. Unfortunately for her, the decision is made and there was no turning back. I'm not sure who I am trying to convince, Cicely or myself. Because I don't want this, I want Austin back in Georgia or wait a year before we move to Phoenix.

Cicely has her mind set on attending Savannah School of Art & Design in Savannah, Georgia. She can get the HOPE Scholarship if we stay here, and that will offset some of her college expenses. It makes sense to wait, so I plead the case to Austin, but he is dead set on us moving to Phoenix sooner than later. He is ready for all of us to be under one roof. Had I paid attention to the obvious red flags, sirens, and firetrucks, I wouldn't be stuck back home in Tulsa.

When Crazy Reigns

School is out and Austin's here. This is it, we're really moving to Arizona. I'm both excited and apprehensive. Cicely flew to Dallas yesterday. It was the first time since she was five years old that she got on a plane and didn't say I love you. I'm sad, I can only imagine her anger and frustration with me. In her eyes, I'm an epic failure as a parent. I wish she could see life through my eyes. I am doing the best I can! This move will be a good thing. For the first time, we'll have a two-parent and two-income household. Why can't she understand that I want a better life for her and Timothy? I love them, they are the reason my heart beats.

Now, Timothy, he's a momma's boy, but Cicely gives me an F for parenting. Dropping Timothy off at my friend Renee's is emotional for me. It's hard to leave my baby behind. He's excited to spend the summer with his cousins. Renee and the boys are outside when we pull up. Timothy quickly jumps out and joins the kids playing basketball.

"Hey, girl."

"Hey Renee." Austin and Renee speak. "So, this is it, huh?"

"Yeah, it is. It's a long drive, but we'll break it up. We're in no rush, I don't start work for a week."

"That's good." I hand Renee money. "Thanks for letting him stay."

"Girl, he's fine."

"Timmy, come here. We're leaving."

"OK, mom."

"I love you, and I miss you already, you are my favorite son, you know."

"I love you too, mom and yes, I know."

"Call me anytime you want to. I will see you soon. Take your bags in the house."

"Ok, mom. I love you." Austin calls Timmy over to talk to him, I see him give him money, and they hug.

"Bye, baby, I love you." My eyes are cloudy with tears.

"Ok, girl, we're out, I love you," I say to Renee. "I'll call you while we're on the road."

"He's fine. I love you too," she says.

Renee and I have been friends since middle school. We moved to Atlanta together. We've raised our kids together. We're more than friends, we're practically family. I know Timmy is in good hands.

"You alright baby?" Austin asks.

"No, but I will be."

"He's good, it's all good baby, let's do this."

The first leg of the trip is relaxing, Austin refuses to let me drive. "No woman of mine is driving a big moving truck," he says. I'm fine with that, no argument from me. Between naps, I do my homework and post for my online class. He's cheerful and optimistic, singing and sharing his dreams the whole way.

We've reached Mexico. Finally, we can get a good night's sleep. Our bodies welcome the softness of the hotel bed. We're dead-tired, but horniness overrides. We make love and crash out. It would be nice to sleep in, but it's not an option. The water feels refreshing to my tired body. I'm laying across the bed while Austin gets dressed. We have a long day ahead of us. I can hardly wait to get to Arizona, get our own place, and see my babies. Austin taps me on the leg, interrupting my thoughts. "Thank you for trusting me with your heart, and you and the kids' lives. I am going to take care of you baby, I promise. You are my rib, my flesh. I've got you, alright!"

"I trust you Austin."

"I can't wait to make you Mrs. Phillips."

"I ready to be Mrs. Phillips."

"I love you baby, what were you thinking about anyway?"

"Us."

"Let's get breakfast and get on the road."

"Now, you're speaking my language, let's eat."

On the road, I drift in and out of consciousness.

"Wake up sleepy head, we're here!" Austin parks the truck on a side street, near several hotels. "Baby, what are you doing?"

"It's late, and I don't want to wake up Skye or try to park in the apartment complex. Let me grab our luggage so we can get in here and get some rest. We have a busy day ahead."

It is scorching outside, even at three o'clock in the morning. We get to the room and set our things down. The room's muggy, so Austin turns on the AC. "Come here, baby." He pulls me close to him and squeezes so tight that I gasp. Welcome to Phoenix, Mrs. Phillips, get used to me calling you that."

"Thank you, baby, I'm glad to be here with you."

"I promise to take care of you and my kids."

"Promise you'll take care of my heart, Austin."

"I promise, I will."

"I love you."

"I love you too." He gently bites my lip, then rolls his tongue over my teeth and invades my mouth with his passionate kisses. We stand in the quiet, embracing. I'm so tired, I could fall asleep standing up. I shower first, then wait for him to come to bed. I know he's exhausted. Austin comes in, turns the radio on, and we snuggle. I feel asleep to GQ "I Do Love You." "… I love you so right now, I love you so right, I love you soo…"

Austin is up early. He's already opened the curtains, and the sun is beaming in the room.

"Baby, get up, we have a lot to do this week. We have to make a decision on a place to live. I want to be out of Skye's by the end of the week. I scheduled for us to look at some houses today. We need to open a joint account ASAP, nothing is separate anymore – we're a team."

Looking for a house is stressful. We go back and forth about where to live, Austin wants to live in Scottsdale to be closer to work. I want to live in Ahwatukee because it's familiar to the kids and me. We look at tons of houses in both areas. We need familiarity, especially for Cicely. She's an introvert and doesn't make friends easily, and people aren't as friendly here as they are down South. I will do whatever it takes to help her adjust, and hopefully, she'll hate me less. I'm not too worried about Timothy adjusting. He's an extrovert and makes friends easily.

The tension between Austin and Skye is growing, I stay out of it and out of the way. In fact, I need to get out of the house now, my nails and toes need attention. We have another home viewing today before Austin goes to work at five; he's out running errands now. Let me text him: "Hey, I'm headed to the nail salon."

"Remember our appointment at four," he writes back.

"Let's meet back here around three, you know I don't know my way around Scottsdale," I said.

"Alright."

I look forward to relaxing, even if it's just for a little while because the air in the apartment is heavy and draining.

But right now, relaxation is a luxury that I can't enjoy, my phone is ringing back to back.

"Hello."

"Where the fuck are you?"

"Leaving the nail salon, why are you yelling?"

"You knew before you left, I told you that we had an appointment in Scottsdale. Why the fuck did you leave any goddamn way?"

"I thought you said the appointment was at four o'clock."

"The guy called and changed the time."

"You should have told him it wouldn't work. I told you where I was going."

"I've been calling your ass for the longest. I know you saw me calling."

"My nails were wet, and I couldn't answer. Baby, calm down."

"Don't tell me to calm the fuck down, your ass ain't here so we're going to be late," Austin is livid.

"I am on my way."

"You can't do a motherfucking thing right! All your ass had to do was be here, and you're out of pocket."

"I am just around the corner, less than five minutes away, you're trippin'. We'll be okay."

"Oh, I left your ass, I am almost in Scottsdale."

"WHAT?"

"I wasn't waiting for your ass, Allie. You

should have been at the house."

"Okay Austin, I'll go back there now. Check it out and let me know what you think."

"You're a fuck up, I don't have time for this shit." I tune him out, and head to Skye's. I am not trying to hear that shit.

"Hey, are you listening to me? You can't get in anyway, because Skye is gone, and I have my keys."

"Is she coming back soon?" I press.

"I don't know. I don't keep up with her like that."

Damn, he doesn't get off until two in the morning.

This is not going to work. Hot tears are streaming down my face. I'm hurt and mad.

"Where are you going to go?" Austin asks.

"I'll to go D's or get a room. I'll see you tomorrow."

He's oblivious to my tears and keeps screaming insults.

"You're fucking stupid and inconsiderate. Just meet me there."

"You know I don't know my way around Scottsdale." Plus, I don't want to be around his ass right now.

"Figure the shit out! If you'd had your ass at home, we wouldn't be going through this shit now!" The few moments of peace and relaxation that I had at the nail salon are a vague memory now. I try to reason with him to no avail. I head down I-10 West towards Scottsdale. Austin hangs up in my face. Fuck him. I need a moment.

Ring, ring, ring. It's Austin again.

"Where are you?" I can hear the venom in his voice, he's fuming. He gives me directions and then starts talking to someone, "Hello sir, how are you today? I'm Austin Phillips. I hear someone talking, but I can't make out what they're saying. Austin sure changed his tone quickly. "I am well, thank you. I'm guiding my wife in, she is unfamiliar with the area. Okay, sir, I'll be right in." He's talking to the owner of the house. He pauses briefly then refocuses his attention to me. "Hurry up and get your ass here! Got me making an excuse for your in-motherfucking-considerate ass." He hangs up in my face again.

I'm unsure of where I'm headed, but I know I need to get there fast. A few minutes pass…ring, ring, ring, ring... He's obviously in the presence of the homeowner, "Hey baby, how much longer before you get here?"

"I am not sure." Though he's using "kind words" I know Austin is still angry. He guides me in, I was about fifteen minutes away. I really don't want to go in there. I need to gather my bearings. I cover my tear stains with make-up. I pull myself together, then get out of the car. Austin walks up, hug and kisses me. I want to pull away from him, but we're not alone.

"Hey baby, you finally made it. I was telling Mr. Scott that you aren't from here and you got a bit turned around." I'm thinking, I bet you didn't tell him you are an asshole. Mr. Scott shakes my hand.

"I apologize for being late," I say sheepishly.

"No, worries, welcome to Phoenix. Come inside, my wife is waiting for us." She greets us at the door.

"Take your time looking around, let us know if you have any questions." *Question: I wonder if her husband treats her like Austin treats me?* The house is nice, but not spectacular. Hands down the backyard is the draw with its pool and spa. This house excites Austin, mainly because it's only ten minutes from work. I am indifferent. I am still absorbing the blows from his verbal assault. We wrap up and walk outside, he wants to talk. I'm in no mood for small talk or any kind of talk for that matter. I am mad as hell and want to slap the shit out of him.

"Let's grab a bite to eat at Shea Medical Hospital. I don't want to, but I follow him. We force a conversation while we eat. We walk to my car, this sucker he has the bravado to try to hug me. I cringe and pull away.

"I love you, baby." I don't respond. This fucker acts like nothing happened. I swear he is bi-polar. I get in my car and head back to Chandler, a city right outside of Phoenix. I am barely out of the parking lot…ring, ring… Damn, what the fuck does he want?

"Follow me to work." We pull into a business complex.

"Park right there," he points to an empty parking space. It's Sunday and still early, so the area is deserted.

"Let's go for a walk," he points out various shops and shares his aspirations for rebuilding his company.

"I started my company just before my unplanned 'vacation' to the Arizona State Penitentiary. I want my dream to come to fruition. I put Antonio on, and his business is booming. I am better at this than that fool. I'm building my clientele, my name is getting out there – I'm a beast at this."

While he's talking, I drift back to how he was when he first got out. He didn't know how to text, or even set up an email account; I taught him how. He notices that I am not paying attention "You're not even listening to me!" I'm startled. "I hate I brought your ass out here." Here he goes on another damn tangent.

"I should have left your ass in Atlanta." I stare directly into his eyes. He shifts the conversation, "You being late today was a bad look for me. I don't appreciate you being out of pocket, you fucked everything up!"

"I get up and walk off."

"Where do you think you're going? You'd better sit your ass down." I keep walking. He follows, belittling and degrading me. He looks at his watch, and abruptly stops, "I've got to get started."

We walk to my car. I get in and drive off.

Reality Check

What have I done? I don't deserve this bullshit! How did I allow Austin to manipulate me into moving to Phoenix? I don't even like Phoenix. Now I am here with this fucking psycho, and my kids will be here soon. I can't go back to Atlanta. I'd have to find a job, a place to live, even worse, I'll have to explain why I'm back. I'm sure Renee will let me stay with her, but I can't tell her what's happening. How will I explain this to the kids? I'm sure Cicely would love to be back in Atlanta. I'm not explaining this letdown to my family and friends. I am too embarrassed to tell anyone about how poorly Austin treats me. I don't have the money to move right now anyway, we spent so much coming here. Hell, I've been out here a week now, and his ass is talking about how he hates that he came to get me. Right now, I do too! What am I going to do? Oh, God, help me!

Have you ever felt trapped and doubted your decisions? Felt hopeless with nowhere to turn? This is my truth. I am a mess.

My thoughts are interrupted…ring, ring, ring, ring…Ugh! "Hello."

"Where are you?"

"On my way to the apartment."

"Are you alright? He acts concerned. I know he's not.

In my head, I respond, *'What the fuck do you think, you crazy bastard?'* What comes out is "Yes." I will not let him know he's breaking me.

"You know, I'm under a lot of stress. I just want everything to work out for us."

Here he goes with these damn excuses.

"I hate living with Skye and working for this pompous asshole Antonio. I love you, and I want things to be good between us."

"We're good Austin."

"You're lying baby, I know you're mad at me Allie.

Don't lie. I promise baby, I'll make it up to you."

"Ok, baby, no problem." We both know I'm lying. How in the hell do I get out of here? How can I leave his ass before my kids get here? We get off the phone, but he calls back three times before I make it to the apartment.

"I'm sorry baby, I feel bad." Now, he's lying. He could have kept that insincere apology.

"Austin, I've got to go."

I need to lay down. I'm mentally drained. I step over the array of boxes to get to the full-sized bed which sits on the floor. We're cooped in this tiny room, it's cluttered with random remnants of Austin's old life and now my things. The walls are caving in.

Today was mentally draining. Tomorrow is Memorial Day, my last day before starting work. I hope it's a peaceful day. I need some sleep. He won't let me sleep; he calls back to back. I finally stop answering and cry myself to sleep.

I don't know what time Austin got in, I'm too exhausted to care.

"Hey baby wake up, I did really good last night, tips were nice." He's standing over me, dangling a wad of money. Let's go eat breakfast. I want to show you Phoenix, Phillips style. "Come on Allie, get up!"

I want peace. We go sightseeing after breakfast, mostly around Scottsdale. Austin is trying to convince me of the benefits of living out here. We drop by his friend's cook-out, but we don't stay long because he's going to work on his day off. He loves money and grinds hard to get it. Now that's one good thing about him, he has a strong work ethic.

So far, we're having a good day. I want it to continue. "Austin, stay home with me tonight," I ask.

"I got to get my bread. Working tonight brings us closer to our goal."

"I don't want to be alone." I set a trigger.

"You don't want me to make money Allie? I keep my mind on my money and my money on my mind. I'm rebuilding, you know that."

If I hear the word rebuilding again, I am going to scream!

He leaves the house and calls right away. I inhale deep, and exhale long. "Yes, Austin."

"Allie, do you want this to work?"

"Yes"

"Do you love me, Allie?"

I paused. I loved who I thought he was, but not the person that he is. I don't answer fast enough. "So, you don't love me, baby? I'm out here busting my ass for you and your fucking kids, and you don't love me."

"I never said that."

"Then why did it take you so long to answer?"

"I don't know, it just did."

"What do you mean you don't fucking know, now your ass don't know shit. See, that's the shit I'm talking about, you don't love me. Why the fuck did you come out here? You could have stayed your ass in Atlanta – had me coming out there, missing money to pick your ass up and you don't even fucking love me. Here we go again, damn!

I want to give you a good life, a life like you've never had Allie. I'm doing this for us. Don't take this the wrong way but you're my bitch. You're mine, I don't like other niggas looking at you. It makes me crazy in fact when you met Israel the other day you were a little too chummy –

cheesing and grinning in that nigga's face. I didn't like that shit at all." I can't believe what I was hearing.

"What are you talking about Austin, all I did was greet your friend – nothing more, nothing less!"

"But I saw how that nigga looked at you – like he could have you."

"Austin you're tripping, I don't want your fucking friend, and I am not up for this shit today." I hung up the phone.

…Ring, ring, ring… I sent it straight to voice mail. Not today! He leaves voicemail messages and then texts. I am tired of fighting with Austin especially about dumb shit…ring, ring, ring…

"Look Austin, tomorrow is my first day of work. I need some rest. Let's squash this and deal with it tomorrow."

…Ring, ring, ring… "I don't give a give a fuck about you having to go to work tomorrow – you're going to talk to me. I want this to work, and you've got to want it as much as I do. The kids will be here next week; we've got to get a place before they get here. I am trying to set things up for us."

"Okay, baby you're right, now let me get some rest! I'll see you in the morning. Good night." Austin calls five more times, I let the voicemail fill up. His level of crazy is increasing.

Austin wakes me up when he gets in. "Do you love me, Allie?" I'm discombobulated, it's late as fuck.

"Yes, Austin."

"Then make love to me." I don't want to fuck him, but I'm so tired of arguing. Sex with Austin is hit or miss. He's a great kisser, and he loves sucking my breast. He's not big on eating pussy, but he's decent. His dick is alright, but he's a minute man. I rarely enjoy it. I love him, so I don't complain, but now that he's getting on my fucking nerves, it's hard to fake it.

Determined to make up for the past two days, so he holds nothing back. He kisses me deep and passionately. He cups my breast then sucks them as if they are nourishment for his body. He bathes my body with his tongue, then opens my legs and spreads my vaginal walls with his fingers – he plays around. Even though I'm tired and pissed off at him I am aroused. I need a good orgasm to relieve all this stress. He licks, sucks and tastes me like I am the last supper. He savors every bit of me. The tension leaves my body; my nipples are erect. I'm getting mentally in tune. "Oh yes, Austin right there. I'm almost there."

Austin stops eating my pussy and slides on top of me. Ugh, I try to stay focused. I feel Austin enter. "Oh my God, baby, you feel so good." He acts as if he's received the entrance into heaven. I need to release, so I imagine a more skilled lover ravishing my body. He gives about three pumps. Oh God, I hope he doesn't cum as fast as he normally does, mid-thought Austin is breathing hard. "Baby I'm cuming, I'm cuming, baby damn. I tense up. I'm sorry, baby your pussy is so good. I can't help it. Damn! He's done. He rolls over, heads to the shower and comes back to bed happy, acting like he just hit the lottery. Meanwhile, I'm heated, and now sexually frustrated. He could have kept that two and a half minutes' worth of needle dick! I go shower, hell I need some sleep.

Starting To Get Messy

I am blind to the fact that I am emotionally and verbally abused. I'm just stuck in love. I keep thinking how much I want to make it work. I miss my babies, but don't want them to come here. But my time has run out. I am guarded, and walk on eggshells. Now that we are in our own place, Austin is a little better, but he's mad that we are in Ahwatukee. The house is big— five bedrooms and three levels, everybody has their own space. Cicely has the bottom level to herself, so we barely see her. Timothy has his space too, but he watches television in our room. We don't argue in front of the kids, so they have no idea how bad it is. I keep them out of his way. I don't want them to do anything to upset him. I'll be glad when school starts, and they'll barely have to see him then. As for now I run an interference. I make sure they have everything they need so that they won't disturb him. We barely see each other, our work schedules are opposite, and he just picked up another day. Sundays are our family day, we're at ease now, but I wonder how long this will last.

Austin is in our room resting, Timmy is in his room playing, and Cicely and I are in the kitchen talking while she's cooking dinner. "Mom, Austin is mean to Timothy when you're at work. He doesn't' think I hear him, but I do. I just tell Timothy to come downstairs with me. I'm keeping my eye on him. I don't trust him," Cecily says.

"I'll be back." I fling the bedroom door open. "Austin, get up. What's going on with you and Timmy, are you being mean to him while I'm at work?"

"He doesn't listen, and he won't clean up behind himself. I get sick of repeating myself," Austin says.

"Why didn't you tell me?"

"Why are you questioning me, I am a grown ass man." I can see that he's starting to get heated.

I leave out and go to Timmy's room. "Hey, make sure you clean your room and listen to Austin."

"I do listen," Timothy says.

"I know how you listen, let's make a plan on how you are going to keep your room clean and keep quiet while he's resting." "Okay, mom," Timothy retorts.

"Come on. Let's go eat," I say.

Austin doesn't come down for dinner. After dinner, Timmy and Cicely go for a swim. Austin leaves. I lay down and doze off. I hear a loud commotion outside of our bedroom door. Cicely and Austin are screaming. I can't quite make out what they were arguing about. Timothy is crying. I jump out of bed and fling the door open.

"What's going on?" Cicely and Austin tell their versions on the story. Timmy's crying and yelling, "I'm sorry, I'm sorry." They are still arguing.

"I'll call the police!" Cicely screams.

"Call the motherfuckers!" Austin echoes back.

"I hate you!" Cicely fires off.

I chime in, "Enough you two, enough!"

Austin snatches Timothy up and drags him down the stairs. I jumped in and pry them apart.

"Keep your motherfucking hands off my goddamn son!"

I startled him, and he let him go.

"You two go to your rooms, now!" Austin turns his rage towards me.

"I can't believe you took their side! I told him to clean his room, and he just sat there and looked at me. I asked him several more times, and he didn't budge. So, I snatched him up to make him clean up that mess, and he screams like I'm killing him, then Cicely comes up the here and curses me out."

The bell rings, and someone knocks. Cicely opens the door and Phoenix Police officers' walk in. "We're responding to a domestic disturbance call." I am outdone. Cicely really called the police on Austin. "What's going on, we heard yelling as we walked up? They ask each of our names, and we each tell our version on the story. They speak to Timothy and look him over to see if there are any visible injuries. All our emotions are high.

The officers ask Austin, "Sir, do you have anywhere to go tonight?" He is livid, but he is very calm in his responses to the officers. "I work overnight. I'll go to work. I'll come back tomorrow once things calm down."

"Ma'am do you and the kids feel safe."

"I feel threatened, I don't trust him!" Cicely made it clear.

"Cicely, were fine. Officer we'll be fine." The police waited while Austin got his things together. Austin mumbles under his breath as he packs his things. "Is everything OK, sir."

"Yes, sir!" Austin leaves the premises with the police officers.

The kids and I talk about what transpired, they're looking for answers that I don't have. I see the disappointment in their eyes and we all go to our rooms. I lay down and replay each step, I can't believe what happened…ring, ring, ring…Damn it's Austin. "Hello."

"I can't believe I had to leave my motherfucking house behind this bullshit. I swear on everything I love that this is some bullshit! What part of the game is this?"

"Austin, I don't have the energy for this tonight. I am still trying to wrap my mind around what happened." This is some BULLSHIT Allie, you know it is!"

"Austin, I am tired, I can't do this right now!" I hang up. What is going on? Why is my life unfolding like this? We are supposed to be here to make our lives better. We were supposed to get married and have our happily ever after. I know this is the beginning of the end. I've got to figure out something to get our lives back on track. I've loved Austin for many years. I'd imagined us being together, but now that we're finally together, life is falling apart. How can I make things better between Austin and the kids and us? I am not sure how we can ever recover from this incident, especially now that the police are involved. One good thing is that I'll be starting a new job in a few weeks. I don't want to go to work tomorrow, I'm mentally drained. I drift off to sleep weeping.

I wake both Cicely and Timothy up before I leave for work. "Look, guys, stay out of Austin's way when he comes home. I really need you to keep the house clean and the noise down. Timmy, if you have an accident pull your linen off the bed so Cicely can wash it. Ok, guys, I am depending on you. I love you both, and I will see you when I get home."

I can sense their disappointment in me for not leaving. I wish that they can understand I have to establish a plan and be very careful in how I execute it, because I know how volatile Austin can get. He hasn't been physically abusive, but he is very mean. They don't know that Austin is emotionally and psychologically scarred from his childhood. It's not their business or my place to tell them that Austin was in and out of foster care since he was three years old. His father was a pimp, and his mother was his bottom whore. She had ten children between him and other johns. He was also physically and sexually abused as a child. They don't know that in one of his foster families, the dad put his penis in Austin's mouth. They won't understand that he was adopted into a family where infidelity was rampant, and the girls were victims of sexual molestation. They didn't know that he was a great provider and that his first and second wives, both left him and took a lot of his money. They don't know about the prison time or about him losing everything. They don't understand how complicated this all is. Cicely and Timothy won't understand that he just wants to give love and receive love in return.

He is working so hard to rebuild his life. The days that Austin is mean, cold, and calculated are the days that his demons take over. They don't understand that the love we have for one another will conquer all of his demons. He just needs time to rebuild, and he needs our support. I return to the present moment… the look on my children's faces lets me know that I am a disappointment to them, and they think that I choose Austin over them. I want to tell them that I have a plan, but I don't, at least not right now. I need to figure things out in time, but I realize I don't have much of it. They both agree to be on their best behavior. I only hope that Austin will be on his. I reluctantly leave for work.

King of the Castle

Austin is barely speaking to us since his return home. I'm not making much effort to mend our relationship since the incident either. We tiptoe around each other. He avoids me at all cost, some nights he sleeps in his car, and in the mornings, he passes by the house and circles the block to see if I've left for work before he comes home.

Some mornings we pass one another, look right in each other's eyes, but don't acknowledge one another. This is crazy, we can't continue to live like this. We're barely speaking now. I've got to do something to ease this tension. I can't lose my family. On top of our issues, the house is falling apart, and we need to move. I swear if it's not one thing it's another.

I am so glad that today is my last day of work. I hate this damn job, this day couldn't get here fast enough. I need this break before I start with the City of Phoenix, plus I want to do something special with the kids before school starts. I've been thinking of places we can go all day, it's a toss-up between the Grand Canyon and San Diego. I'll give them two choices, and we'll have a family vote to decide which direction we'll head in. I'm excited about taking a mini vacation, we can certainly use it. I can hardly wait to get home to share the news. I'll talk to Austin first, then we'll meet with the kids.

On the drive home I pray. *Dear God:*

> *Please mend our relationship and to help our family heal. We need a fresh start all around. Thank you for giving our family the opportunity to get things right. Thank you for the new job and for having enough money to take a mini-vacation. I love my children and Austin and just want our family to get along. Lord, if Austin is not who you have for me then let this relationship end amicably. Thank you, God.*
> *Amen*

This is just what we need: a new house, new job and a new outlook on life. I am smiling. By the time my prayer ends I turn on Frye Road. I'm ready to share my good news. Austin's car is in the driveway, it's sparkling clean as always. He leaves the space in the garage for me. One side of the garage is filled with our unpacked things, empty boxes, my washer, dryer, and refrigerator. I turn into the driveway and hit the garage door opener, gather my things and go inside. The house was very quiet and clean. I am at peace, and overly excited to talk to Austin. I walk into our bedroom, Timothy is sitting on the floor watching cartoons. Austin is getting ready for work. He is ironing his white dress shirt.

"Hey mom," Timothy says without turning his head from the television.

"Hey." I'm smiling.

"Baby, I need to talk to you about something!" "You do? Well, I need to talk to you about something too, let me go first."

I sit on the side of the bed facing Austin. He walks around the ironing board, grabs his shirt, puts it on and buttons it up. It is ironed to perfection, very crisp with perfect creases down the sleeves. He puts his cufflinks on and stands directly in front of me. Beads of sweat form on his forehead. His hair is freshly cut, and the line of his edge up is razor sharp. He leans into me, places his hands on my thighs, and quietly but sternly whispers "Consider this your thirty-day notice." I'm shocked. "What?"

"I am leaving you in thirty days, I am putting you on notice." Speechless, I blankly stare right into Austin's cold, sad eyes. "I HATE you, I HATE your kids. I should have never gone to Atlanta and brought you here, I HATE EVERYTHING about you, I don't even like dark-skinned women! In fact, I hate dark-skinned women. If my mother were alive, she'd be shocked that I was dating you."

My heart sinks, I'm in disbelief. I am dazed and temporarily check out of the conversation. I cannot believe the words that Austin is spewing, especially considering the fact I never heard anything like it in our over twenty-five-year-long history. Austin even lived with us when he was a teenager. When I tune back in, Austin was still talking. "This is how it is going to go down, for the next thirty days, I don't want you or your kids saying anything to me. I won't say any anything to y'all either! I will do my best to try to be gone before you come home from work and will try to stay out of the house until you leave in the mornings. I will appreciate it if you all will just stay out of my way when I'm here."

This is a lot to decipher. "Why thirty days?"

"That will give me enough time to get me a place.

You and the kids can stay here."

"But we've already made plans to move." "You can call the landlord and tell him that you decided to stay," he's spewing venom.

"I can't afford this place alone," I interject.

"You'll figure it out." Timothy is still watching cartoons in our room. Our voices are low, but our emotions are high.

"Perhaps, I can help you with some money for a few months." I'm thinking do you really think I trust your ass?

"Now, what was it that you want to talk to me about?" I look at Austin like his head is spinning off.

"Allie, what do you want to talk to me about?" "Nothing."

"Nothing, what do you mean nothing?"

"Never mind, it isn't important." Austin keeps asking what I want to talk about. I keep responding nothing, never mind, or it's OK. Austin looks at his watch and realizes that it is time for him to go to work.

"Shoot I've got to go, we'll continue this later." Austin leaves. I sit motionless. I'm sure thirty minutes has passed, I haven't moved. I am in shock, and I am numb. A variety of emotions are brewing inside of my mind.

Ring, ring, ring, ring... Ring, ring, ring... ring, ring, ring. It's Austin. I don't answer. Everything is moving in slow motion. One tear creeps out of my right eye then slowly rolls down my face and drips from my chin unto my Ann Taylor cream-colored dress. I refused to let Austin see my pain, disappointment or tears. I know I have to plan to get the hell up out of here. Does this fool really think that I was going to stay for thirty days and watch him walk out on us?

Ring, ring, "Hello."

"Why haven't you been answering my calls?"

"I don't want to talk. I'm still processing our conversation."

"Well, I want to know what you wanted to talk to me about?"

Are you effing kidding me? "Why, it is relevant now? It really doesn't matter at this point."

I'm irritated that he asks me this dumb shit after what he just dropped on me. I really see now that Austin is a serious mental case.

"But, what was it?" I break and tell him about the vacation plans.

"I thought that it would help mend our family and would've been something fun for the kids before school starts." But it seems my prayers have been answered, but I don't mention it to Austin.

"Then why didn't you say that when you walked in?" Austin acts confused.

"I tried to," I say plainly.

"You could have stopped me."

"No, you were pretty adamant about getting your point across, so there was no need to say anything after that point."

He sounds agitated, "We could have avoided all of this if you had stopped me and said what you wanted to say!"

He is no more agitated than I am, this conversation is futile.

"It's too late now, you've spoken your piece. I am glad to know how you really feel about me and the kids. I've got to go!"

Click. I sit in silence.

Escape Plan

What am I going to do? I can't go back to Atlanta a failure, this is embarrassing. I don't want to move back home; too many bad memories there, but I don't have a choice.

I just need to regroup maybe only stay for six months. I need a job ASAP. I surf the internet. I can't

believe it – this job is perfect. I've held this position twice before. God, you are working! I know this job is for me. I just need to get an interview, if I get an interview, I can get the job.

I am overwhelmed, I lean my head back on our large camel-colored leather and wood headboard and sigh. Let me call Chasity.

"What's up Allie?"

"Hey, Chasity!" I attempt to sound jovial, but I fail.

"What's wrong with my girl, do I need to come to Arizona and beat somebody's ass?"

"Naw, but I'm coming home, and I need a job fast. I'm sending you my resume right now. I saw a position at Community Action Project, do you know anyone there?"

"I'll actually will see the director at a meeting

tomorrow, I'll personally put your resume in her hands."
"Thanks Chas, I love you."

"No problem, are you alright?"

"No, but I will be, I've got so much to do. Let's talk tomorrow after your meeting. Love you and thanks again."

"I love you too girl, bye."

Then, I call my sister, Shannon. "Hey baby girl."

"Hey, sissy."

"What's wrong?" "I'm coming home."

"Come on home, what do you need me to do?" "I need a job."

"Call your niece and send both of us your resume. We're on it!" "OK." I well up inside, my chest is pounding, and my eyes are burning. I am working overtime to hold back the waterfall of tears. The tears are fighting to be released, just like I am from the emotional jail Austin has locked me in. I want to tell her all the terrible things that Austin said to me and how cruel he is. How I feel like a big fool for leaving my life in Atlanta and following this jerk across the country, and in less than two months our relationship is in shambles. I crave for a shoulder to cry on and for listening ears, but I can't let Shannon know that I am such a mess. Instead, I say, "OK, thank you, I love you. I will get my resume to the both of you tonight. I'll talk to you soon."

"Ok sweetie, you don't have to talk about it now or explain yourself to anyone, I love you, bye." I just realized that Timothy had left the room. I wiped the tears from my face, there's no time to breakdown now. I pull myself together I've got the kids and me out of this mess alive.

I call Brittney. "Hey CCL, what's up?"

"Hey FPL, GUUUURRRL!!!!!!! I'm coming home!"

"Really? OK, what do you need me to do?"

"I need a job!"

"OK, have you thought about Head Start? I'll ask momma if they have anything – but I know you'll probably want something in administration, huh?"

"Yes, I've looked at their website and saw one position that I am interested in. Chasity is going to an event tomorrow, and she is going to speak to the director about me."

"Oh, that's cool. Does she know the director?" "I'm not sure."

"Send me your resume, and I'll ask around. When are you trying to come home?"

"ASAP!" I say.

"Oh, OK, is Austin coming?"

"Hell no! I'll get my resume to you tonight, thanks Brit, I'll be in touch soon."

"OK, I'll talk to you later."

Brittney was my oldest friend. We'd known one another since we were three years old. Our friendship had weathered many storms and overcame some great obstacles. We were more than friends we were truly family. Our families live across the street from one another. Her mother is my surrogate mother. When we were kids growing up in the eighties, we thought we could rap. Our rap names were Chocolate Chip Lover and Freeze Pop Lover, we called one another CCL and FPL for short.

Funny, not one person asked me why I'm moving back home. Perhaps they saw something in Austin that had eluded me, or maybe it doesn't matter to them, they are here for me no matter what.

I really don't want to go back home, but there is absolutely no way I can go back to Atlanta like this. I am a mess. I've got to have an A-1 game plan, and I've got to execute it soon. Damn, it's almost nine o'clock. I'll look again tomorrow. OK, what do I need to do now – pack!

I've got to pack up this house. On that note, I grab boxes from the garage and start packing our bedroom. Dang, this closet is crazy full, I am already tired looking at these clothes. I snatch groups of clothes off the racks and hang them in the garment boxes. The process is moving quickly. It's the adrenaline. I am standing here cleaning out my closet, and my internal closet is overfilled with mess. I don't have time to deal with this right now. I'm building boxes and throwing shit in them – shoes, purses, weave, jewelry and accessories are flying everywhere…Ring, ring, ring… I ignore the phone. I am on a mission to get this house packed up by morning before Austin gets in from work. I move from my closet to our bathroom, this is tedious! I don't have the luxury of time, so I quickly throw stuff in boxes. As I complete packing boxes, I move them to the living room.

I swiftly pack up Timothy's bathroom and move on to the kitchen and the living room. Where did all this stuff come from? You don't realize how much you accumulate until you have to pack. I pack a few items in the upstairs guest bedroom. Timothy's asleep, so I pack around him. I am glad he is asleep because I don't want to nor do I have the time to answer any of his hundreds of questions. I pause for a moment to watch him sleep peacefully. I wonder what he is dreaming about. I want him to know how incredibly sorry I am to have him and Cicely in this awful predicament. Timothy really likes Austin. I believe more than anything he is starving for a father. His father is completely absent from his life. The closest image to a father is my dad, but they only see him once or twice per year. Timothy craves a father's love and guidance. Austin was very nice to him at first – heck, he was really nice to me at first too.

I just want Timothy and Cicely to know that I love them and even though I don't always make the best decisions, I love them both more than life itself. Even if it means moving back to Oklahoma, then that is what I have to do.

I'm not sure how many hours have passed. I am operating on adrenaline, frustration, and disappointment. I want to breakdown as I look over the mass mess of boxes, clothes and other household items, but I can't stop, it has to be done. At this point its life or death. Cicely comes upstairs from her chateau. She sees all the boxes and doesn't say a word. I imagine she is probably ecstatic that I had finally come to my senses. Her heart is most likely dancing in jubilee. The boxes are probably music to her ears, the music will soon stop when she finds out we were going to Tulsa, Oklahoma instead of Atlanta, Georgia. I can't tell her now. She looks around at the small catastrophe and disappears back downstairs.

I continue packing, and Austin continues to call. It hit me, he may come home early especially if I don't answer the phone. I look over the crowded living room and find a small opening on Austin's couch, I sit down. Let me get my mind right to call him. "What's up Allie? Why haven't you been answering my calls?" I'm thinking why aren't you working and why the hell are you calling me anyway? You hate dark-skinned women remember?

"I haven't really been in the mood to talk. What is it, what do you want Austin?"

"I was just checking on you." Austin is serious... Checking on me? Are you fucking kidding me? After everything you said to me, you have the gall to want to check on me. Wow, he is unbelievable. He's crazy. I am working hard to keep my composure, and he is truly testing me right now.

"I'm good, mentally drained but I'll be fine." In my opinion, there was not much left to say, we just needed to part ways. We sit in silence for about two minutes.

"I'm going to rest Austin."

"Okay, Allie." He is trying to stay in my head or break me down. Or perhaps he is trying to figure out my next move. I am not responding how he would typically expect me to respond, so he is a bit thrown off. The last thing I remember was laying down across our king-sized bed.

I awake to Austin standing over me. His form slowly comes into focus. "What's all this, Allie?

"What are you talking about Austin?

"What's all these boxes and everything all over the house, you leaving me? I thought I told you thirty days."

"No, Austin you are leaving us, but you need thirty days. Do you actually think that I am going to walk around here on eggshells for the next thirty days and adhere to all of your foolish demands then watch you walk out of our lives?" I sit up in the bed with my back leaned against the leather headboard.

"I need thirty days."

"That's you. You don't have to be with me, that's fine, but you are crazy as hell if you think that I'm staying here for thirty days."

"Where are you going?" "Does it matter?"

"Where are you going Allie, back to the A?" Why did it matter as long as I am as far from you as humanly possible I thought. "Look Allie, I need thirty days to get my own place."

"Go live with Skye!"
"You know I'm not doing that!"
"Well, I really don't care what you do!"
I get out of bed to wash my face and brush my teeth.

"Look, Austin, I don't want to fight with you. I'm depleted! I get it, you hate me and my kids, you hate I came here, and you hate that you came to Atlanta to get us. It shocks me that we've had a long history and I don't recall you ever hating dark-skinned women. You even lived with my family at one point – you were so kind and humble then. You are the love of my life, I never thought that we'd end up like this! I'm done! I'm hurting, and I'm done!"

Austin just looks at me and goes to the bathroom to shower.

He's very meticulous about his morning routines. I get in the shower after he's done. I come out of the bathroom and grab clothes to put on, Austin walks over and put his hands around my waist.

"I'm hurting, Allie. I didn't want this to be like this."

We stand partially draped in our towels, weeping amidst the mounds of boxes scattered all over the room. Austin wipes the tears from eyes and cheeks, "Don't cry, Allie." I cry harder.

I am more angry than afraid or even hurt. I am angry that I love him, trusted him and have allowed my children to see me being treated this way. Even more so, that they are being treated this way. I am angry that I left Atlanta following his ass. I could have stayed and been just fine. I gave everything up for Austin!

Austin grips me tighter and he kisses me. "I'm sorry, Allie."

He removes my towel and makes his way down my body. He cups my breast in his hands and sucks them, he kisses my stomach. He drops to his knees and licks and sucks on my vagina like he is at a Sunday buffet at Golden Corral. I am crying, yet my body quivers from the stimulation. On his knees, face buried in my vagina, he backs me into the bed. I am weak. I hate him for all the things that we are going through. I am unsure of what he is capable of anymore, so I comply. He is very intentional in how he touches me, he wants me to have an orgasm. A half-hour passes, and he's still eating pussy. I have multiple orgasms. We are both emotional. This is notably his best performance yet. That's just it, I know it is a performance.

I am drained and energetically connected to him, but I know I can't fall into his trap. He looks up at me, "Don't leave me Allie, please don't leave me baby."

He buries his head back between my legs. I disconnect. "Stop it, Austin! I can't do this, please get up, please!"

"Why are you stopping me, Allie? Let me make love to you."

"There is no love here remember, you hate me and my black, dark skin." The tears flow, and I can't stop them.

"OK Allie, OK, if this is what you want!" He stops, the kindness and tenderness instantly fade. Back to cold and calculating.

"You're not leaving for thirty days!"

"Whatever, Austin, get off me!" I squirm from underneath him and go shower again. The water runs over my entire body as I wash the experience off. I want the scent of him gone. It reminds me of him exploiting my weaknesses – him and sex.

Have you ever been torn between loving someone and hating them at the same time? Have your emotions ever clouded your judgment? Have you ever been afraid to face your ugly truths about a relationship coming to an end? What did you do? How do you keep going when your world falls apart?

Roadblocks

It's getting late.

"You're going to be late for work," I say to Austin. "I'm not going in."

Damn, I need to finish packing, but he won't leave my side. In bed, he holds me close all night. Austin is gone when I wake up. I quickly get myself together and start packing again. He comes back within the hour.

"I don't know why you're still packing. I told you

that you aren't going anywhere." I ignore him. Austin stays close to me all day. I can barely go to the bathroom without him following me.

"Austin I'm running to Target."

" I'll take you," he responds. "That's OK, I'll drive."

"No, I'll take you!"

"Austin, I'm very capable of driving myself."

"I'll take you Allie, I'm parked behind you anyway, come on. I reluctantly get in the car with Austin…Ring, ring, ring… I don't answer.

"Why won't you answer your phone?"

"I don't want to talk to anyone."

We pull in Target's parking lot.

"Are you coming inside?"

"No."

I am relieved, but I don't show it. I get out of the car and quickly walk inside the store. I call Chasity back. I briskly walk up and down the aisles, come on Chas pick up!

"Hello."

"Look, I don't have much time to talk, Austin will hardly let me out of his sight now that he knows I'm leaving him. So, you've got to talk fast."

"Are you okay?"

"Yes."

"I did see the director today, and she wants you to send your resume directly to her."

"Yes!" I squeal while picking up the packaging tape I came for. I continued to walk down the aisles briskly and grab a few other things...I know if she gets my resume, I can get an interview and get the job. I live and breathe this stuff. I am so happy.

"Thanks Chas, I'd better get out of this store before Austin comes in looking for me. I love you, girlie."

"Allie, are you safe?" I can hear the concern in her voice.

"Chas, I don't know. I'm trying to get there as quickly as I can. I am doing whatever it takes including having sex with his ass. I hate it, but my babies and I have to get out of here safely. I love you. Pray for me Chasity. I'll see you soon." I hang up the phone, check out and walk to the car.

Austin is sitting with the car running, I get in the car with my bags and thank him for driving me. He pulls off, but he doesn't head towards home. He drives through the parking lot to the back of the store and parks the car.

"What are you doing Austin?" I nervously ask. At this point, I don't know if this fool is about to do anything stupid. I don't know if he has a gun. I know he's a felon, so he isn't supposed to own a firearm, but these days I can't put anything past him.

"Why are you doing this Allie? Why are you leaving me?"

"Austin, you put me on notice."
"I was frustrated with how things are going between me, you, and the kids. I feel like you all exclude me. I am still mad about the police coming to my home."

"Austin, I can't change that. You walk around angry every day; you barely speak and nearly everything is a problem especially with Timothy. Then you get angry with me and accuse me of taking sides. These are my babies - I have to protect them. I don't know what you are capable of."

"Protect them? I would never hurt them!"

"They don't know that and neither do I. We can't keep living like this. There is no turning back. I cannot undo what's done and I can't get out of my head what you said. What do you expect me to do?"

"Give us another try Allie, please we can work this out."

"What?!"

"Give us another try; we can start over. Let's get another place to live and start fresh. We can go to Scottsdale this time or wherever you want to live." His desperation is showing.

"Austin, I can't. I don't see how that will work. I don't trust you, and the kids don't like you. You hurt their mother, and you've betrayed their trust in you."

"See Allie, you won't give us another try."

"Really Austin, really? I can't believe you are trying to make this be my fault. I cannot win with you. Please, let's just go back to the house."

"No! Not until you'll say that you will give us another try."

"Austin please, not this!"

"Allie, I love you and my kids. Y'all are my family. I don't want to lose my family. I'll do what you want me to do."

"Wow, you are unbelievable! Please let's go to the house, Austin." I am not sure what to do, Austin eventually pulls off and we drive home in silence. Conversations with Austin are exhausting. I just want out and to go somewhere where the kids and I are safe.

A Dressed Up Mess

Over the next few days, Austin tells anyone that will listen that I'm leaving him. He wants sympathy. A couple of our mutual friends give unsolicited advice to try to convince me not to break up with him. They're unknowingly co-signing to Austin's bullshit. They don't know the dark details of our relationship. They only know what we show them. They were privy to one incident that

occurred back in 2009 when we were visiting Tulsa, I guess they'd forgotten about that.

Austin takes off work for the third day. I'm never going to get out of here at this rate. Oh, I know what to do, I'll have his friends in Tulsa convince him to move. He loves, respects and trusts them. Austin calls them to bitch about me leaving, they're on speaker phone. I but in, "Hey– we can start over together in Tulsa. Roger, Austin can work with you." I shocked everyone.

This is the first time any of them hear me say anything about us staying together and moving to Tulsa. Roger is particularly excited. "I love that idea!" he has been trying to get Austin to move back home for years. Now were ganged up on Austin, three to one. "Y'all can stay with us," they say over the phone.

"I don't know about that," Austin retorts. He's hesitant, he hasn't lived there in over twenty-seven years.

We work him at all angles. It's a tough sell. I go in like my life depends on it. "Let the kids, and I go first, get established, and you can stay here stack some racks and then come. By that time, I will have a house, and you can come do your thing in T-Town. You can work with Roger a little while, then start your business in Tulsa. You can come back home, baby. We can do this!"

I speak his language. He loves money, and he loves being in charge. Roger and Peggy are on board co-signing for Austin's return. Finally, he agrees reluctantly. He's not fully convinced. I've got to seal the deal. He is lying in bed. I climb on top and straddle him. I kiss his head, neck, and chest. I work my way down his body, kissing and stroking him. I want to throw up, but I have to convince him that I am serious about making us work. I unbutton and unzipped his Khaki shorts, grab and stroke his penis. I put my mouth on it.

"Hey guys, we're going to talk about this and give y'all a call back later." I lift my head, "Thanks for everything guys, well talk to y'all soon."

I act like I love having him in my mouth. I moan and groan, that excites him. He pulls me up, "I want to feel you." So, I take my shorts and panties off and sit on his little penis. I ride it like the Oklahoma Cowgirl I am. In a couple of minutes, if that long, Austin is through. I climb off him and jump in the shower. Austin is blissful. He loves feeling my black sweetness wrapped around his caramel- colored dick. He is in a good mood now. He falls asleep, and I pack while he sleeps. I am leaving Phoenix by any means necessary.

Austin is still in a good mood today, things are easy. Austin and I set the plan, he's driving us to Tulsa this weekend and comes back for good in two months. He wants to work through peak season. I agree. I reserve the truck to pick up on Wednesday. Austin and his friends will load the truck.

At last, I am getting the heck out of Phoenix. I hate living here. Austin went to work tonight. I finally get some space and peace. I'd sent my resume to the Head Start

Director at Community Action Project, and she said we'd schedule the interview once I was in Tulsa. I am happy, but still cautious because Austin is going back and forth on his decision to move. We pick the truck up today. We will pack this evening since it will be cooler. Austin is wavering, he's having second thoughts.

"Baby were doing the best thing for our family," I say. His friend is here and we're all packing. Whew, this seems like the longest week ever. My girlfriend Lynne stops by to see what's going on. Things are happening so fast, I forgot to tell her that I am leaving. Austin stalls every time his friends attempt to load the truck.

"Lynne, I don't want her to go, I don't want to lose my family," Austin says.

"Austin don't start that now, we have to finish loading the truck baby, come on now."

Lynne attempts to mediate, "Can we just stop and talk for a while, let's pray."

Are we really having an intervention? My mind is made up, I am too close to the finish line. Fuck what Austin, Lynne or anyone has to say. I can't believe this, we are having a prayer session right in the living room. Austin seems to calm down a bit. To keep the peace, I agree to stop for the night. Just because I agree to stop doesn't mean I've changed my mind. Austin's friends and Lynne leave. I am livid, but I know not to show it. I shower and go to bed.

Austin has the audacity to think he is getting some ass tonight… humph, not in this lifetime. I cut that shit off quickly, and we sleep on opposite sides of the bed.

I am tense. I am ready to go, and he keeps stalling. We discuss the plan again. At sunset, we load and drop off Austin's things that he is taking to Skye's house. Now it's time to load my things. His friend is back to help load the truck. The momentum is going, and all is well, then Austin loses it!

"Fuck this shit! I'm not going to no motherfuckin' Tulsa, God Damn Oklahoma! This is some bullshit! What part of the game is this? Your bitch ass thinks you're slick don't you?"

I am in no mood for this shit. I keep loading the truck. Austin is livid, he's yelling, cursing, ranting, and raving. I am focused. He keeps on.

"Enough Austin, you don't have to fucking go, just leave us alone." Austin keeps yelling and cursing, he throws his cell phone at the truck and takes off walking down the street.

"Fuck you, you fucking bitch, I hate you!" His friend shakes his head and walks behind him.

The kids and I are left alone to load the truck. "We've got to do this, no matter what."

"We're good mom." We keep packing. We move all this heavy ass shit – the refrigerator, the washer and the dryer.

Lynne calls to check on us. "What did y'all decide to do? Are you going to work things out? Are y'all going to Tulsa or staying in Phoenix?"

"Girl, Austin had a meltdown and left. The kids and I are packing the truck now."

"Oh, damn. I'm at work, I'll call Adrian to come help."

Lynne and I live around the corner from one another, so she sends her son and one of his friends to come over to help. We work hard, and pack until the wee hours of the morning.

Lynne stops by after work to check on us, but she is tired and goes home. My bones are aching, but we keep going until everything that we own is in the truck. We're down to our toiletries and the clothes we are planning to wear tomorrow.

We are all exhausted. I take the boys home; they were a lifesaver. The kids sleep with me on the floor of my room. In the still of the night, I lay here in deep thought.

My poor babies, they do not deserve this mess, they don't deserve a mother like me. Why am I living my life in reverse? I am empty inside. I am a skeleton of who I used to be. I cry and pray for my babies and for me.

Dear God, why is this happening? Please help me. I drift off to sleep. I get up early in the morning to call the rental company to rent a tow for my car since Austin isn't going to drive the truck anymore, now I have to drive the truck across the country with my car on a tow dolly.

Everything I own in the trailer. Lynne follows me to get the hitch. I return to get the kids. We say our goodbyes to Lynne and embark on the longest, most eventful trip of our lives.

I feel the guilt of yet again uprooting our lives and starting over again. Why did I leave Atlanta? Many years will pass before I truly recognize the undeniable damage that I did to my children. At this very moment, I just want to get as far away from Phoenix, Arizona, and Austin Phillips as I possibly can. The crazy part is that despite all we've been through, I still love him.

Have you ever loved someone that you know was toxic for you? Why do we love what doesn't love us? Better question, why do we love people who don't love themselves? Can it be that there is a lack of love for ourselves?

I believe that if I love him enough, I can fix him.

Hell, but in the process, I've become broken. I am a dressed up mess at the pinnacle.

Through all this chaos, I am still in school, and I have to post while we're on the road. I stop to gas up and post. My Facebook notifications on my phone are going off like crazy. My cell phone, like me, is broken and barely hanging on.

"Cicely, pull up Facebook on my laptop." She logs in and I grab the computer from her. I am mortified as I read all the posts and inbox messages from concerned friends and family from across the country checking on us. The first message that catches my attention was from Jamal, my ex-fiancé. He is checking to see if the kids and I are safe because Austin accused of us messing around. I can't bring myself to respond. Austin has access to my page, he posts that I left him and that I cheated on him the entire time we were together with Jamal. He calls me bitches, whores, and everything imaginable. His entire intent is to embarrass and hurt me. Goal accomplished. I can't believe the level of betrayal that this deranged nut goes through to hurt me. What have I done to him besides love him? He is a sick man, and the craziest thing is he doesn't know it.

I remember asking him after one of his rampages if his family and friends knew that he was crazy, and he smugly said, "No, I don't act like this around them." Shortly after that incident, I contacted one of his closest friends during another psychotic episode. He told me: "Allison, I love Austin like a brother, but you have to leave him. Where is he now?"

"In the house," I said.

"Where are you?"

"Walking up and down the street." "You need to leave!"

"I can't! My keys are in the house, and I don't want to go back in. He is acting crazy as hell. I am not sure what he is going to do."

"Get somewhere safe tonight, but I mean you need to leave him for good. It is the best thing for you and your kids." I thanked him for talking to me and wandered around in the middle of the night for another hour waiting for him

to fall asleep or calm down. I'm ashamed at my reality, because this happened to me when Austin lived with me in Atlanta. I know you're thinking, *'Damn, girl what the fuck is wrong with you?'* All the signs were there. I snapped back to reality, read a few more post and messages, and then made a post to my Facebook page:

To my friends and family who are worried about the kids and me, we are fine. I left Austin and he has access to my Facebook page. The posts are from him. I apologize for the fear and confusion that our private mess becoming a public matter has made. Pray for our safe travels. I will let you know when we reach our destination. Thank you again for your care and concern. We are safe, and I love each and every one of you. I post for class, gas up the Penske truck and continue our long, tiring, eventful journey to Tulsa, Oklahoma.

Austin can't call me since he threw his phone at the truck, so he is harassing me through my inbox.

Austin writes: I've been trying to remove all of your pics, fam, friends, etc. Off of my page. When you get a minute do the same.

Austin writes: The next time before you start talking to your ex-boyfriend at least wait until you're out of the man's house, but it's all good. Peace. You tried to trick me to do all that work for you, see how God worked?

I write: Leave me alone, he just asked how we were and I said fine. I didn't even accept him as a friend. I put all my love and energy into you and you misused it. I would never treat you the way you treated me.

Austin writes: You got that. I will leave you and your sweet family alone. God bless you and have a safe trip home. I've already prayed for your guys. Peace, joy, and happiness for you guys. And please, lets never speak again in life. This will make me happy. Thank you.

Austin writes: Please forgive me I'm glad you're happy. T-TOWN DO THAT SHIT GIRL.

Austin writes: Cleaning up my space right now was hoping to have heard from you by now. Allison, I do love you. I don't know if we can move forward. I'm here because you left baby. I would have never left you no matter what, that's just me. I would rather work through it. I don't want to have no one else but you, but I have to keep it real, I believe you made your decision by leaving. Is Tulsa more important than us being together? It must be really safe. I'm set in my ways, and now I'm back to win the race, no matter what. Holla back, only if you won't quit on me. I love you, holla sucker.

Life In Reverse

I wake up dazed and exhausted. My heart and soul are in pain. I am completely empty and depleted on the inside. I am a shell of myself only going through the motions. Is this really my life? I can't believe I am here, in my parent's house. I should have kept going. I don't feel like discussing why I left Austin and came to Tulsa with anyone. Funny, no one, not even my parents ask. I am literally torn between two worlds. I hate Austin for everything he's put me and the kids through. I hate him for my current predicament, yet I still love him. The love I have for him started over 25 years ago as a school girl crush in this very house. *Oh, God why? What happened to him? What happened to me? Life…*

Donald can't save me from his friend, he's been dead for over eighteen years, murdered on the streets of Tulsa, Oklahoma. His murder is still unsolved. Life! God, why? Why did you bring me back here? There are so many horrible memories of this place, too much pain to bear. I must get my life back on track fast and get out of here.

Have you ever been brought back to the very place that you vowed you would never go again? Have you ever questioned God? Asking why your life is where it is?

My nephews and Shannon help unload the truck into the storage unit. I return the truck and get a refund after all the mechanical problems I had with it, that made our 24 hour trip, 41 hours. Did I mention the A/C broke twice in the middle of summer?

My niece Ivey offers to let us stay with her and her family. About four family members offer for the kids and I to stay with them. Everyone in the family knows how funny acting my mother can be and want to save me from the drama, especially in my current mental state. Heck my dad looks like he is happier than a kid in a candy store 'cause the kids and I are here. Y'all should see the look on his face when I announce that the kids and I are moving to my niece's house. I think he is going to cry. Heck, a tear may roll down his face. He was looking forward to getting a break from being in the house alone with my mother. That's a damn shame. He should have handled this situation years ago. Everyone knows she runs him. He is desperate for company and companionship. Oh, well I ain't up for the shenanigans.

I am never disrespectful to her no matter how mean she is to me. I don't allow her to treat my kids like she treated me as a kid. I established boundaries years ago and we are not about to break them. It is best that I don't stay here. We move in with my niece. Day one, I look for a place to live. I contact the Head Start Director to let her know that I'm in town. I have a lunch interview on Monday at Ted's Escondido Café on 71st Street in Broken Arrow. I interview with her and another Director. It goes well, and I got the job offer on the spot. I am happy, I make more than I have ever made in my life. Tulsa's cost of living is cheaper than Atlanta's and Phoenix's. Things are looking up. I view properties daily. I successfully enroll the kids in school. Maybe I needed to come back home. I need to heal, that is one thing that I am certain of.

I work my way through the transition and try to keep it together for all of us. It's overwhelming, guilt creeps in – old guilt over moving around a lot. We move at least once a year, packing and unpacking boxes is our way of life. My kids have no real sense of security, as soon as

they get comfortable in one place, it's time to move. I've got to get a handle on why I'm unsettled and unstable.

The one constant in our lives has been the church. No

matter where we moved to in Georgia, we attended the same church. One of the toughest challenges of leaving Georgia was leaving my church home. We'd attended New Hope Missionary Baptist Church in Powder Springs, Georgia since 2002. My faith and church family provide a sense of belonging – at least at times it did. I was an active member, but only close to a few members, and not many people were aware of my constant struggle with stability. Now, living in a new place, I don't have that religious structural support. I visit several churches in an attempt to find the sense of belonging that I felt with New Hope. I visit Shannon and Ivey's church, and Chasity and Cara's church. I attended school with many of the people in the pews. The church is popular in the community and it's growing. I attend a few Sundays, then join Metropolitan Baptist Church. I don't feel the down- home, genuine connection like I did at New Hope, but it's better than nothing.

My life is looking up, except Austin is harassing me. He calls about thirty times a day and if he isn't calling, he is texting or Facebook inboxing about how much he loves me, misses the kids and I, and how sorry he is.

Austin writes: Allie, I wish things were great with us, but they are not. I really feel like I tried to make things work out no matter what. I'm sorry, no bullshit. I'm happy for you. I must live on, I can't keep putting myself through pain. We're messed up yes. God bless you, see you at the top. Peace. I still love you. I'm going to get back what the devil stole from me in 2006 – my life. One love Wonder Woman, there goes Batman. Peace.

I write: It's a shame that your insecurities got in the way of what I though could have been a beautiful thing. I am hurt and disappointed, but time will heal the wounds. I hope that you are restored at 100% and that you find the relationship that you want with someone that you will cherish. It hurts like hell, but I finally realize I was never that person for you. I love you and I am certain that you will always have a special place in my heart because I have loved you for a long time from afar and up close.

Take care, Allison

I occasionally answer his calls or respond to his messages. Most of the time the calls start out the same. "Hey baby, how are you?" I miss you Allie, why did you leave me? I would have never left you no matter what. You left me high and dry. I wouldn't have done that to you. I was trying to make it work. I love you, and you left me – you took my kids from me. I can't believe you, Allison."

Remember you put me on a thirty-day notice, you hate me and my kids... you hate dark-skinned women. Your words Austin, not mine!?

Bitch rolls off your tongue so easily I can't be too many more bitches. Plus, you left the kids and me to pack the twenty-six-foot truck alone." Austin doesn't want to hear anything about what he did to contribute to the demise of our relationship. He only wants me to know he wants me back and how badly I did him.

Within the first few minutes of the conversation, Austin gets angry when I don't respond to him like he thinks I should. He goes from Dr. Jekyll to the crazy ass Mr. Hyde. "Fuck you, bitch! I know you are back with your ex anyway. FUCK you. I hate you BITCH. I don't even know why I called you!" Click.

Ring, ring, ring. I don't answer, he apologizes to the voicemail and texts "I'm sorry Allie, I love you." If I don't respond, he curses me out again via text. This is our daily routine.

Shannon can't take it anymore and interjects, "You're going to have to stop answering the phone if you want him to stop calling you."

"If I don't answer he will call back to back, he won't stop calling!"

"Yes, he will, I used to work in a building with FBI agents, and when Raymond was stalking me, they told me what to do. It's like they get a thrill or high when you respond. It's just the fuel they need. If you give them just a little attention, they will run with it. You are going to stop answering sissy, I know it's hard baby girl because you still love him, and your heart is still in it. You are going to have to be strong. It's for your own sanity. Trust me, I've been there."

I know she is telling the truth. It's hard not to answer Austin's calls, some days I fail.

I am tired of being called a bitch and being threatened. It is getting easier and easier to ignore his calls. I'm almost to the point of not answering at all.

But damn, I have a financial crisis and who better to ask for assistance than Austin. Hell, he owes me. I took care of his ass the whole time that he was in Atlanta. I think that fool contributed $800 and you would have thought he provided $80,000. I held down half the load while I was in Phoenix. Shit, I'd even given this fool my son's cell phone – he still has the number to this date. He is going to help me. I break down and call. Austin answers on the first ring, "Hey A, what's up?"

"Hey Austin, I need a favor I need $400."

"For what, and why are you calling me, ask one of the dudes you fucking with?'

"Because it is the least that you can do after all the shit you put me through." I'm torn. I don't want him to have anything on me that will prolong our need to communicate, but I need the money. I've got to get it back to him ASAP.

"I'll give it back to you when I get paid in two weeks."

"OK Allie, look I need my shit back!" Says the man that is at least $6,000 indebted to me. Wow, motherfucking unbelievable.

"Austin, are you going to give it to me or what?"

"Yeah Allie, I've got you. You know I still love you, are you going to be my woman again? If we were together, you wouldn't have to ask me for anything. I'd give it to you. Business is picking up Allie. I am rebuilding, watch you'll see!" My stomach is queasy at the thought of being with him.

"Austin, I am not going backwards, are you going to give me the money or not?"

"Are you going to tell all those busters that are trying to holler at you that your man is back. Put it on Facebook."

"I'm not playing with you Austin, forget it." "Allie, stop tripping I've got you."

"I need you to wire it." There was no way in hell that I am giving this nutcase my address.

"Ok, I'll take care of it before I go to work." "Thank you, Austin."

"I love you, Allie. I will never stop loving you – you are bone to my bone, flesh to my flesh – God's word."

Oh God, is he for real?

"Let's not do this Austin."

"Alright Allison, I'll send you a text when I do it." "Thank you, Austin. Austin texts the Western

Union information with a note, "You'd better let them busters know we're back together." Why did I accept money from him? I just made a deal with the devil. Austin calls regularly. He texts and inboxes me. He thinks the money is his way in. He really thinks I am getting back with him. Hell can freeze over, and it still won't happen.

Two weeks pass, just enough time for me to think about whether I am sending the $400 back to Austin. I am, I don't want to deal with him any more than necessary. I got paid today, but I can't make it to the bank before it closes. I'm in route to an event with Chasity at the Mayo Hotel. It's a rooftop cocktail hour, then were heading to an indoor party.

Ring, ring, ring. "Hello."

"Hey, Allie it's Friday, have you sent my money?"

"Hello, Austin, how are you? Good, I am well thanks for asking?"

"Did you send my bread?"

"No Austin, I did not I just got off work, and I'm headed to an event, I will send it Western Union tomorrow." I can barely get my words out before I am interrupted.

"You said today, tomorrow won't work." He is

talking to me like he is a pimp and I'm his bottom whore.

"Tomorrow will have to work. I will call you in the morning. Austin."

"Allie, I didn't hesitate to send it when you asked for it. Now, send me my fucking money today! Fuck that event, you are probably going with that bitch Chasity. I hate that BITCH! I always have. People tell me that they see you two bitches at church."

There it is – his favorite word to call me. If I didn't know any better, I'd think that he believes Bitch is my real first name, middle name, and last name. I can tell that this isn't going to end well.

"Austin, I am not trying to hear all of that, I'll call you tomorrow."

"No, bitch you'd better send me my bread today." I hung up the phone. Somedays I wish that I could slam a cell phone like a good ole' house phone. I shake him off and go on to the event. Austin calls back-to-back for two hours. I ignore his calls. I am having a decent time, the ambiance is nice, but my phone rings non-stop.

I notice a call from my mother coming in. Before I can answer, she hangs up and calls again. I think it is an emergency because she calls back-to-back, "Hey mom, is everything okay?"

"Allison, do you owe Austin some money? He just called here very upset and said you borrowed money from him and won't pay him back. He said you're using him."

I am LIVID! I see red for the first time in my life. Literally, I must have blacked out! The audacity of that nutcase to call my mother and bring her into this MESS! I am done, 38 HOT!

"I told him I'll give him the $400 back," I say to my mom on the phone. I step away from Chasity and the group to have some privacy. I walk down the corridor to a semi-secluded area.

"You better not send him a freaking dime!" I am so mad that I can barely see straight. I feel my eyeballs burning. The tears are welling up. I am so tired of Austin hijacking my life. He is so overbearing. This is it, no more. I finally reach my boiling point!

Has anyone every violated your life so bad that you had to reclaim your peace?

This is where I am with Austin. He has done so much collateral damage that I have to stand my ground. Any further damage will be my death sentence.

"Mom, I have to go. Don't answer your phone if he calls back. I am getting ready to call him!"

I've had enough. I can't pull myself together to go back to tell Chasity that I am leaving. I walk out of the door and down West 5th Street to the parking lot. I am absolutely besides myself, this fucking jerk! I loathe him with my entire being. Everything that Austin put me through since we reconnected surfaces. I hate everything about his insecure ass! I cannot believe that this motherfucker called my damn mother.

I call Austin, as soon as he answers I yell "Something is seriously wrong with you. You are one crazy fucking nutcase! Why in the hell did you call my mother?"

"'Cause you won't answer your phone. I knew that would get your ass to call me back."

"You are sick, leave my mother out of this, do not dial my parent's house again you fucking idiot!"

"Fuck you, BITCH! Send me my God Damn money.

Hanging out with that bitch Chasity, fuck both of you

BITCHES, both of y'all fucking every nigga in that church. I know about you. I've got people watching you!"

"Fuck you, Austin and whoever you've got at Metropolitan Baptist Church watching me, fuck them too!

117

I've had ENOUGH, this shit has got to stop with you! You've gone too far now!"

"Send me my money, and we never have to speak again bitch."

"I'm not sending you shit, fuck you!" Click.
Ring, ring, ring.

I don't answer. I drive down the Broken Arrow Expressway until I reach my exit at 129th East Avenue and 51st Street. Austin calls at least fifteen times in the twelve minutes it takes me to get home. I zip through the neighborhood, pull into my driveway, and press the garage door opener. I am hotter than fish grease. Thank God the kids aren't here. Timothy is at Chasity's house with her son Brian, and Cicely is with her cousin Alona. I shut the garage door and go inside. I walk straight to my bedroom and undress.

Ring, ring, ring.... I let it ring until I get in the bed. I am comfortable at home. The house is quiet, and I am at peace. Ring, ring, ring. So much for peace, "What the FUCK do you want?" I am ready for whatever Austin has in store tonight. I am done with him treating and talking to me anyway he pleases. He has no respect for me, and I have to put an end to his harassment and disrespect.

"Oh, so now you answer your fucking phone, it's about time bitch."

"No, Austin you are the BITCH! All you do is bitch like the little weak, little dick BITCH that you are? "What did you say?"

"You heard me you little BITCH!" I feel the venomous rage inside me.

"Allie, you are going to make me hurt you."

"Hurt me? Fuck you! You already have. You can't do any more damage Austin!

"You forget you're in my hometown, Allie. I will send someone down there and put an end to all of this."

"Did you just threaten my life, Austin?"

"Yes, you know the deal. I have a long reach. They don't call me Easy for nothing. You know what's up!"

Something takes over me, like a dark force rising. I go on a rampage. "FUCK you Austin and any of your little flunkies.

I wish you would send some of those weak ass punks here for me, please do! They won't make it back. In fact, since you have been acting crazy since I left your weak ass. I record all of our calls so if I come up missing both PPD and TPD will know to come looking for your ex- con, felon ass! Bring it you deranged BASTARD! Did you forget that this is my hometown too? You are not the only one from Tulsa, motherfucking Oklahoma fool! I live here, and my family is here. REAL FAMILY! My two nephews are 6'4 and over 350 pounds each, they will break your little ass in two if I have a hair out of place. Fuck you, you punk ass BITCH, and that goes for you and anyone you think you want to send for me! 'You wanna rumble with the B huh? I'll drop a hex on your whole family, dressed in all black like the Omen – have your friends saying, this is for my homie.'"

Why I am quoting Lil Kim lyrics? I didn't know, but I know I am done with Austin's reign of terror over my life. It's his life or mine, and in this moment, I am not afraid to die. Right about now, I will kill him!

I mean every word I say. My words petrify Austin.

"You are CRAZY. I didn't know that you were so crazy. I can't believe you. I thought you were a good girl.

You went to Booker T. Washington and look how you are acting. I thought the T-girls were good girls and you're crazy!'" He's shook.

"Did you think you had crazy on lockdown? You aren't the only one that can play crazy, but I am not playing! If you come down here or send any of your friends to Tulsa – there is going to be some slow singing and flower bringing. Fuck with me if you want to bitch, it's your life or my life, and I'll bomb first! I've got kids to live for! Come for me if you want to, tell your family bye before you do BITCH!" Click.

I don't know why I am quoting Biggie Smalls and Tupac lyrics either. I guess it is a 90's gangsta rap kind of night. This motherfucker overlooked my gangsta. I'm from Tulsa, Oklahoma, stop sleeping on me. He let the smooth taste fool him. He'd never meet my other side until tonight. He doesn't call back. Finally, I am at peace. I lay down and laugh to myself. I just shed two hundred and fifty pounds of terror. Ding-dong the witch is gone; the wicked witch is dead... at least symbolically. Now, I am on some Wizard of Oz ish!

Disco Dan

Homecoming is tonight, it's been over 20 years since I attended one of Booker T. Washington Hornets sporting events. This is much different than when I was in high school. Everyone is tailgating, and there are big parties and events scheduled all weekend. People are in town from all over the country to attend the game. I see classmates and other people that I haven't seen in years. I ran into my girlfriend Delana. She invites me to her birthday party in two weeks.

It's Delana's birthday weekend, and my friend Carlos is in town from Atlanta. "Hey, Allie, what's up for tonight?"

"Shannon and I are going to my girlfriend's birthday party, wanna go?

"Yes, I'll hang, where's Brittney?" "I'll call and see what she's up to."

"Alright, bet." Carlos picks us up from my house. "Britt can't make it. She has other plans."

"Alright, I'll catch up with her next round," Carlos says.

"The party is at the biker club on Peoria, you do remember your way around right?"

"I see you've got jokes." "I'm just making sure."

We arrive at the party, about an hour passes and they're ready to go. Shannon wants to go The Living Room, it's a small hole in the wall that is about the size of a living room and den combined. Seriously, it's literally an old gas station and convenience store, perhaps a 7-11. The bay where the pumps once stood are still in tack, and cars park in the like they are getting gas. I remember one-time Chas, Renee and I went there when we were in town for our 20th Class Reunion. Renee walks up to pay the cashier and says, "Let me get five dollars on pump one and a bag of Doritos." We burst out laughing, but she didn't find it funny! We laughed about it for most of the night.

The Living Room is a popular spot, it's been around a long time. Probably because there aren't many nightclubs or places to hang out in North Tulsa. Anyway, Carlos, Shannon, and I leave Delana's party and head there. The crowd is OK – not packed, but steady, and the DJ is jamming. One thing about the Living Room there is always someone to dance with. Now, it may not be someone you want to hook up with, but you'll have a good time if you like to dance. We find a table right in the front near the dance floor. We order drinks from the waitress and sit and catch up. Carlos knows Austin and asks what's up with him.

"So, Allie what really happened between you and Austin, why you leave him?"

"Don't go there." Please don't go there.

"For real, it's like that?" "Yes!"

"Wow." Carlos looks disappointed.

"'I'm done talking about it."

"Okay, chill." I quickly change the subject, the last thing I want to do is to spend my night talking about Austin. No way it's going down like that. Carlos alternates dancing with Shannon and me, the men in the crowd probably can't figure out which one of us he's with. It doesn't stop them from asking me to dance, I spend a lot of time on the dance floor.

Back in my wild clubbing days in Atlanta, I was particular about who I'd dance with, because it could have led to a hookup. But as I get older, I am more interested in dancing. I am the lady that will dance with the guy that all the other ladies turn down. I figure everyone is out to have a good time, it's not hurting me to dance with him. It may make his night. It's not as if I have to go home with him or sleep with him. To keep him from hanging around once I finish dancing I just say, "Thanks for the dance, see you later."

I can spot the cheap ones a mile away. If a guy doesn't offer to buy a drink, whether I want one or not – he's cheap and needs to keep it moving! If I dance with him through three or more songs and I leave the floor, and he tags along just to take up space and air, I walk off. I go to the bathroom or talk to my friends. Better yet, if a guy friend is there, I go dance with him. Sorry dude, you don't get to dance my happy feet off, then stick around and suck up air and space, knowing good and well he sees the beads of sweat rolling off my forehead and doesn't even offer a drink. He's blocking any and all other potentials from coming my way... Boy Bye! Someone needs to teach these busters club etiquette – if there is such a thing.

Tonight is cool though, no straggly busters. Shannon and Carlos are dancing, and I'm sitting at the table bobbing my head to the music. A deep baritone voice penetrates my ears.

"Would you like to dance?" That cologne, umm he smells good! I look up into the eyes of a thin, sort of tall, caramel-colored, bald guy. I give him the once over – he's wearing a white button-down shirt with fancy embroidery, a pair of jeans, and dress shoes.

"Sure." He grabs my hand and leads me to the dance floor.

"What's your name?"
"Allison, what's yours?"
"Danny."
"Nice to meet you, Danny."
"The pleasure is all mine," Danny is a pretty good dancer, and I can tell he loves to dance just as much or even more than I do. He is quite theatrical. He moves around a lot and takes up a lot of space. I love dancing, so I am fine with his antics. The DJ is on point, and he's playing a great mix of old school and current hits. He keeps the crowd on the dance floor. I lose count of how long we dance. I'm having a wonderful time. He spins me around, circles me, and pulls me close to him. He hops, dips and slides. He's busy.

I laugh to myself, "You're quite the dancer Danny."
"So are you," we laugh.

Other patrons are watching us, and some are cheering

us on from their seats. The DJ even gets in the mix, he makes a few comments over the microphone. I look over at Shannon and Carlos, and they're pointing and laughing at us. I laugh and wink at Shannon. Danny really likes to dance! We danced so long we had danced up a sweat.

We take a break from dancing and walk back to the table.

"What are you drinking?"

"Coconut rum, pineapple juice with a splash of cranberry juice."

"I'll be back." "I'll be waiting."

He returns with my drink and several napkins. He hands me my drink, wipes the sweat from his face, then hands me a few of the napkins. I introduce him to Shannon and Carlos. He sits with us. *Return of The Mack* by Mark Morrison comes on, and Danny says, "That's my jam," he grabs Shannon's hand and asks her to dance. Carlos and I join them.

The four of us stay on the floor for at least six songs, we exchange partners. As Shannon and I cross paths she says, "Yes, you go back to "Disco Dan."

We laugh. That is a perfect name for him. We dance,

talk, and drink until the lights come on. We walk to the door, "It was nice meeting you. I really enjoyed your company."

"I enjoyed yours too."

"Do you want to go to breakfast?" "No, thanks."

"I'd like to keep in touch, may I have your number?"

With the lights on, I can see him much better. His bright, white teeth are perfectly straight. His oval shape face is narrow, He stands around 6'1 or 6'2, and his frame is very thin. His eyes look sad – they turn down on the outside corners. I can't tell if he is sad or sleepy. In the light, I see that he is quite a bit older than I am. He isn't old and decrepit, but more distinguished. I give him my number, and he walks me to the car.

"It was really nice meeting you, get home safely." "You do the same."

Carlos and Shannon are in the car waiting. I get in, and they clown me about Disco Dan! Carlos drops us off and goes back to his hotel room. I am tired, I rush to get ready for bed.

Danny asks me out several times. I decline each time. I'm not interested in dating anyone. I am still shell- shocked after Austin. I need to heal after that madness, plus now is not the time to bring anyone else in Cicely and

Timothy's lives. I don't have time to date anyway. I am busy with the kids, work, and school, my hands are full, and my time is limited. I am not sure that I even knew how to date anymore. Plus, Danny is quite a bit older, I've never dated anyone that much older than me. Austin is the oldest person I've dated, and he's five years older. I've always heard that old men give you worms. True or not, it's stuck in my head. One of my girlfriends dated an older guy, and I always gave her the blues about it. Now here I am with this guy 16 years older than me, wanting to date.

Danny is persistent, he doesn't give up easily. I'm out shopping and pass Abuelos Mexican restaurant, hmm, I wonder how their food is? I want to check it out. Hey, I'll let Danny take me there.

Danny calls to ask me out, I accept his invitation and recommend Abuelos. Will Thursday work for you?

"Yes, that perfect, I'll meet you. I'll be in a light blue Solara."

"Okay, I'll see you then."

"I look forward to seeing you."

"Same here." I really look forward to seeing him, he's

a nice guy.

He calls when he arrives, "Hey you, what's your status?"

"I'm parking. He walks to the car and opens the door to greet me. This is the first time I've seen him since we met. I catch a whiff of his cologne – the fresh, crisp scent is enticing. Damn, he smells good! He is incredibly handsome! How did I overlook how fine he is? His eyes look happy tonight, the outer corners still turn downward, but they are lively. So maybe he was sleepy and a little tipsy at the club. His eyes are light brown, not quite hazel, but a light hue. I am not sure how I missed this the first night either. His pearly whites are glistening, they are so straight that they look fake. His tight grip helps me out of the car. He hugs me, and I smell his fresh breath and cologne.

"Wow, you look amazing." "Thank you."
"How are you?"
"I'm great, how are you?"
"I'm well." We go inside Abuelos, and the hostess greets us. There aren't many people in here, so we are seated immediately.

We sit in a booth facing one another. The waiter

introduces himself and takes our drink orders. He returns with our drinks and takes our food orders. We talk, he looks me directly in my eyes and then scopes out my body. He focuses in as if we were the only two people in the restaurant.

"Thank you for finally accepting my offer, what changed your mind?"

"I wanted to eat here." We laugh. I'm so serious. We share a little about ourselves. He stares intensely, sort of seductively, it makes me a bit nervous, but I can't let him know that he gives me butterflies, so I stare back at him.

"What are you staring at?"

"You, you are beautiful, I am just taking it all in."
"Thank you, you're handsome."

Our food arrives, we talk over dinner. I have to post for class, so I can't stay out too late. However, I am enjoying his company. It's been a while since I've been out on a date and engaged in normal conversation with a seemingly sane man. He is a nice distraction. However, that is exactly what he is – a distraction.

"Can I see you again?"

"I'm not interested in dating." I have my elevator speech ready.

"I have no room for dating. I have children. I'm in school, and I work full-time. I work out several times a week. I spend the little spare time I have with my parents, and occasionally I hang out with family and friends. See, I have absolutely no room for a man in my life."

After this laundry list of reasons, I am sure he lost interest. I have a lot of baggage. He takes my hands into his.

"When do you take time for you…to relax and enjoy life?"

This is a foreign question to me. What is that?

Have you ever been so engulfed in life that you forget to live?

That is me. I have so much to do that I can't focus on the present and the gift that it is. I shrug, "I don't know, I guess I don't." I hate that I said that as soon as the words leave my mouth, I want a do-over.

"I used to be like that, too caught up in life to enjoy life." That strikes a chord. My life has been so crazy the

133

past few months that I haven't lived much, I've been kind of just existing. I am not about to share any details about my life with Austin, and how I ended up back in Tulsa with Danny. This area of my life is completely off-limits to everyone, especially some guy that I just met and not interested in going any further with anyway.

"I have schoolwork, and I need to get home."

"Oh, I've got me a smart one, you're educated!"

"Yes, I am, and you're lucky that I am taking the time to spend this evening with you."

"Oh, really?"

"Of course, I thought you knew?"

"Ah, I see." We laugh and wrap up our evening. We walk to my car, he thanks me for the evening and hugs me. Oh, God, he smells so good! I am weak for bald heads, straight teeth, and a good smelling man. Let me get my ass out of here before I get in trouble.

"I had a good time tonight, Danny. Thank you."

"No, thank you, the pleasure is all mine... can't wait to do it again."

"I see you have jokes, good night." I head home. Not a bad date, it was kind of nice and refreshing. But I do not have time nor interest in dating. It's out of the question. My focus is on getting my life back on track. I make it home in ten minutes. I go in the house, and I settle in.

Ring, Ring, Ring.

"I made it home. I enjoyed your company."

"I enjoyed you, Mr. Jackson."

We chat a moment, I remind him that I have to post for school. We hang up, I shower, post and go to bed.

Something New

Chasity is hosting the Old School, New School Prom event in a few weeks and wants me to attend. She's taking her new guy. I pass on the offer. I'd have no interest in being the third wheel.

"Did you ever go out with the guy, Danny?"

"Yes, we went to Abuelos. We had a good time, but I am not interested in him like that."

"You should invite him," Chasity insists.

"I'd rather not, you and Ron go and enjoy yourselves."

"Come on Allie, it will be fun!" "I'm busy with the kids and school."

"Timmy can stay with Brian. So, Timmy is taken care of. Cicely hangs out a lot with her cousin, can't she go over to her house or can she come over to your house?

Now, see the kids are good."

"I am not sure what Alona is up to, Cicely can stay at home alone if I decide to go."

"So, you should ask Danny to go, it seems like he likes you. I'm sure he'll love to go."

"I don't care if he'd love to go or not, I am not going!" A few days pass, and Chasity asks again. The answer is still no!

Danny and I talk on the phone from time to time. He asks to see me again, and I decline. One evening my key sticks in my front door, the kids and I try to get it out to no avail. I call a friend, but get his voicemail. I leave a message. I call Danny to see if he will come get it out.

He's right on it. He was on his way. I keep tugging at the key and shake it loose.

I call Danny, "I got it out."

"I am already on the BA, I can come on over to check it out to make sure it doesn't get stuck again."

"No, that's okay. I am sure it will be fine." "Are you sure, I'm almost there."

"I'm sure, thanks though."

He sounds disheartened. He turns around and goes back home. My friend comes over once he gets the message. We hang out a while before he leaves. A week before the event Chasity asks, "Did you ask Danny to go?" I am tired of her asking. "No, I haven't, but I will."

Austin is calling again, I will not answer his calls, so he leaves messages.

"Hey, Allie, this is Austin. How are you and the kids? I pray that you all are doing well. I am calling because I need to get my Cartier glasses from you, call me." I can hardly believe that this fool is calling me about some glasses he gave me two years ago. I won't call him back, now he's texting. He's being nice because he wants something.

I invite Danny to the dance, he accepts. I give him the date and location and agree to meet him there. Now, I have a reason to shop. Who am I fooling, like I need a reason to shop? I find the perfect dress, a Nicole Miller, taupe, after-five dress with a jeweled belt. What a steal, I get a four-hundred-dollar dress for thirty-five dollars! What an adrenaline rush, almost orgasmic! Ivey's doing my hair.

I'm excited about seeing Danny again. I enjoy our conversations, and we both love to dance.

Austin's calling daily. I finally take his call. "What's up A, how is T-town treating you?" "Good, I got your messages."

"Yeah, I need my glasses back." "Ok, Austin."

"You can meet my sister Jackie and give them to her."

"Have her to call me." "Ok. Alright Austin, bye."

"A, you know I still love you." I'm silent. I can't respond or get caught up in this bullshit with Austin.

"Hello, A, are you still there." "Yes."

"Oh, I guess you don't want to hear that huh?" "No, I don't."

"Well, that's how I feel, and you can't control how I feel. I still love you." He tries to drag me in, but I resist. I tell myself, girl, don't get pulled into his crazy.

"Well, bye then."

"Bye, Austin." Yay me, I did it! I resisted getting caught up in Austin's craziness, I almost got suckered in, but I didn't! Jackie calls me to arrange to meet to get his glasses. Turns out she is attending the same event on Saturday, I'll bring the glasses with me. I need to remember where the glasses are as I never wore them other than to appease Austin and to take a few selfies in them. I find the glasses in a box at the top of my closet. I pull them out and set them on my dresser so I'll remember them.

I am applying the finishing touches to my makeup. Ring, ring, ring.

"Hey, Chas."

"I'm confirming that Danny's coming." "Yes, we're meeting there. I'm heading out shortly."

"I'm already in route, I have to be there early," Chasity says.

"Okay, I'll see you there.

"Ok, chica."

I check myself in the mirror, damn girl you look good! My hair is flawless. My Nicole Miller dress fits perfectly, and the shoes matched the dress to a T. My jewelry coordinates with the jewels on the belt of the dress, and my make-up is on fire. I look amazing. I can really see the weight loss. I grab Austin's Cartier glasses off my dresser. Lord knows I don't want to forget them and have to deal with his annoying ass. This is it, the only thing left of Austin's in my life. Well, I still have his leather headboard, but if he wants it, he can have that too, if it means I never have to hear from him again. I place the glasses in my purse and head out the door. I call Danny on my way to the Greenwood Cultural Center. He's getting dressed.

"I'm on my way, call me when you get there, I'll meet you at the front."

"Will do, I'll see you soon." "Okay."

I stop to pick up Shannon, she isn't ready. I have a cocktail while I wait for her to finish. We listen to music and chat. I flat iron her hair while she puts her make up on. Finally, she slips on her dress. Perfection, we look amazing, and I am ready to go party! We get in the car, I turn the radio up and we cruise down the highway until I pull into the parking lot of the Greenwood Cultural Center.

We're early – this is new for me! We inform the lady at the door that we're Chasity's guest. Part of the perks of Chasity being the mistress of ceremony is a free table.

Chasity is bustling around the stage when we walk in. She spots us and comes to greet us.

"Where's Danny?" Chasity's badgers me.

"He's meeting me here remember, Where's Ron?"
"He's somewhere around here. Here's our table right over here."

"Ah, a front table, cool."

We set our things down and take a few pictures. Chasity's other guest arrive – her daughter and some of her friends I've never met before. Ron comes over the table, and we all sit and talk.

Danny calls. I excuse myself from the table to go meet him in the lobby. He looks debonair. I am surprised that we're coordinated. He's wearing black dress pants, a black dress shirt, and his jacket matches the color of my dress. He is handsome, and he looks even better dressed up. He is such a distinguished gentleman. He hugs me and kisses my cheek.

"Wow, you look amazing," Danny says.

"Thank you, handsome." His eyes attentively glaze over my body. I feel him take me in from head to toe. He observes every strand of hair to every curve of my body.

"You clean up well, and you're intuitive, we're matching," I say.

"Indeed, we are, great minds, think alike."

He hands me a dozen yellow roses. "For you." I smile, "thank you."

Nice touch. I'm impressed. Note to self, he's thoughtful.

We go inside. He must have counted each woman at the table as we walk up. He takes the roses from my hand and presents each lady with one as he makes his way around the table, introducing himself. They are all impressed and thank him for the roses. For a moment, I feel a little slighted, but quickly realize what a true gem of a gentleman he is. He shares my dozen roses so that none of the ladies feel left out. He makes his way back to me and hands me the remaining roses. Then he pulls my chair out for me so I can sit down. He pushes my chair in and sits next to me. Chivalry is alive and well.

"It's nice to see you again, beautiful." "Likewise," I say.

He briefly chats with Shannon then turns back to me. Chasity comes over, and I introduce them.

"I've heard so much about you, nice to finally meet you Danny," Chasity says.

"Nice, to meet you as well."

Danny and Ron, Chasity's husband, chopped it up a while, and then he turns his attention back to me.

"You really look nice."

"Thank you, you look very handsome." He smiles, his perfect weatherman teeth sparkle like stars.

"Well, thank you, come on, let's dance." We're in our element. We dance for several songs. It's obvious he's been practicing on his dance moves. He is all over the floor. He dips, slides, hops, and steps to countless songs. He spins me around, holds me close and glides across the floor.

Once again there is audience participation, onlookers cheer us on, smile and point at us. The energy only fuels Danny's excitement to deliver. I am not sure who enjoys dancing more, him or I. Chasity and Ron join us on the floor and we all dance as if we're the only ones in the room. After about ten songs we make our way back to the table. Danny disappears, he returns with a drink in both hands and napkins. He remembered what I like to drink. This guy is really trying to get in good. He hands me my drink and wipes my face. He dances with each lady at the table that doesn't have a date.

While Danny is burning up the dance floor, I sit and talk with other guests. My phone rings, Damn, it's Austin, why was he calling instead of Jackie? I grab my phone and purse and go to the lobby.

"Hey, what's up?" "Jackie said she is there."

"Ok, she could have called me I'm here."

"Yeah, I know," I ignored the comment, I can tell that there is more that Austin wants to say, but he withholds because he wants his glasses.

"I'll call her and figure out where she's sitting. I've got to go Austin."

I hang up and call Jackie, she doesn't answer. I walk back into the room towards my seat.

"Allison," I hear someone call my name. I turn towards the voice and immediately spot Jackie and her husband seated at the table just before mine. I smile and greet them. Jackie stands, hugs me, and her husband extends his hand out, I shake his hand.

"It's been a while."

"It sure has, you look great. Have you lost some weight?"

"Yes, I'm down about fifteen pounds, it's a work in progress, I want to lose twenty more."

"I saw you on the dance floor, but didn't realize that was you. Looks like you're having a good time."

I laugh, "Yes, I am." We continue small talk for a couple of minutes and take a few pictures. "Here are your brother's glasses."

Jackie tilts her head and forces a half grin as if to say 'I know what you're thinking, but he's my brother, and I can't talk about him with you. Trust I know, he's bat ass crazy.' At least that's how I take it. I laugh to myself, say my goodbyes, and go join my party at our table. Danny is sitting at the table sipping his drink.

"Hey, you."

"Is everything OK?"

"Sure, I just stepped out to take and call and ran into some old friends on my way back in." There was no way I was ever mentioning Austin to Danny. Tonight is amazing! We dance, talk and dance some more. The night ends we say our goodbyes to everyone at the table.

Danny walks me to the lobby. "Where are you headed?"

"Home, I'll drop Shannon off and then home and to bed, I had an awesome time, thank you for coming."

We hug, and Danny pecks me on the cheek. He walks us to the car, and I offer to drive him to his car. He declines and heads off into the night. On the ride home, Shannon and I recap the festivities. I drop her off and drive down the street to my house. I go to the house shower and settle in for the night.

Ring, ring, ring.

I smile, I bet its Danny telling me he's made it home. It's not.

"What's up Austin, I gave your glasses to Jackie."

"I know Allie, she told me. I just want to tell you to thank you. That was big, I really appreciate you."

"It's all good, Austin."

"I heard you had you a date tonight, you're dating old men now?" There he is, the Austin I know. He couldn't wait to get what he wanted so that he could revert to his true nature – vile, mean, and hurtful. Not tonight, I'm on an incredible high from my evening with Danny and will not entertain his madness.

"Goodnight Austin." Click.

Surprisingly, he doesn't call back. Danny did call, and I end the night talking to him until sleep creeps in.

The next day Austin calls, but I won't answer, so he sends me a Facebook message.

I send him a message saying, "no problem" and leave it at that. But why did I respond?! He calls back-to- back, but I won't answer, so he leaves vile messages on my phone. I send him a message telling him that he needs professional help and to please leave me alone. His famous response is "Fuck you, bitch."

I don't respond. This is the last correspondence that Austin sends me.

Home For The Holidays

It's been years since I've spent the holidays in Tulsa and today I'm hosting Thanksgiving in my tiny duplex. I'm not tripping, it will work. I'm excited to spend time with family and friends. Now, convincing daddy to let me host is another story, it was no easy task, cooking is his life! But I did it! I got him to agree to only bring the turkey and one side dish – the rest of us are handling everything else.

Everyone is bringing a covered dish or dessert, except for those who can't cook – their contribution is money, its best this way. I invite Danny to join us, and he's stopping by later. No, we're not dating. We just talk a lot on the phone, I like his conversation.

Shannon and I clean and prep food, while Cicely and Timothy clean their rooms. I check their progress, surprisingly Timothy's room is clean.

"Can I can go outside and play?"

"Go ahead, but don't go too far and don't go in anyone's house."

"Okay mom, I won't," he darts out the door. I knock on Cicely's door and turn the knob, it's locked.

"Unlock this door." I hear her scuffle out of bed. She cracks the door open. I gaze past her, her room looks like a hurricane, tornado, and typhoon tag-teamed it.

"Get up and clean this room." She looks at me and takes a deep breath like I'm bothering her. I'm not in the mood for her attitude.

"Get up and clean your room now," and check your attitude." She rolls her eyes.

Why is the child trying me today of all days? "I am, what is the big deal anyway? It's not like anyone is going to come in my room."

"The big deal is because I told you to do it, I shouldn't have to tell you to clean this filthy room in the first place," I yell.

"You're always making a big deal out of nothing." I push the door wide open and go in to check her. Shannon comes down the hallway to see what the commotion is. She sees the filthy room, and tears into Cicely's ass. I walk out, Shannon follows. Cicely insists on talking shit to me, "I

151

hate this fake family, I wish I were born to a normal family!"

Cicely is one of the most miserable children that I've ever seen in my life. Anytime I address her issues, she has a full-blown meltdown. She accuses me of abusing her as a child and of hating her. This shit is so old, we've been dealing with her bipolar ass outbreaks for years. I am the target and cause for everything that's wrong in her life. It doesn't matter who the real source is, I'm the ultimate blame. Here we are in a full out yelling match...

"Get the fuck out of my house," I say.

She slams and locks her door.

"I will tear this motherfucker off the hinges if you don't open this goddamn door. You don't pay any mother fucking bills around here, open this damn door right now!"

"Leave me alone, I hate you!" Can you believe this girl won't open this door?

"That's fine, I've got something for your ass." I go to the kitchen and grab a screwdriver out of the utility drawer. Shannon jumps in, "Let me handle it."

"Somebody better handle her ass." Cicely knows how to push all my buttons, and she gets a rise out of doing so. I'm in the kitchen in a frenzy, cursing, and mumbling to myself.

"Who the fuck does she think I am? She's got me fucked up!" I hear Shannon talking through the door, "Cicely, Cicely open this door and let me in. I'm not playing with you girl, I am not your mother."

I hear the door creep open. Shannon goes in the room and shuts the door.

Mental health issues are real and need to be addressed. However, in families we often ignore them, don't know how to or want to deal with them. The results are often emotional volcanos that erupt into yelling, screaming, cursing, or other threatening behaviors. Most of us hide our mess and act like these types of issues don't exist in our families or homes. The tension grows and often lead to dysfunctional interactions and our relationships suffer. I admit, I don't always know how to control my emotions and Cicely is an overly sensitive child, so our relationship has suffered for most of her life. I don't always know how to parent her and admitting this ugly truth makes me seem

153

inadequate. Licenses or degrees are required for almost everything we do in this world except being a parent, the absolute most challenging and rewarding job on Earth. God help me! She hates me and expresses it at every opportunity that she gets. Though tough to admit as a parent, there are times I feel the same way. I am sad that our relationship is damaged.

We walk around like ticking time-bombs waiting to explode at the slightest disagreement. There is no time for our apocalypse today, guests will be arriving shortly. I'm not finished cooking and cleaning, and I need to get myself together. Shannon emerges from Cicely's room. She gives me an empathetic look and shakes her head.

"She'll be alright." Honestly, at this point. I am not interested in the outcome of their conversation. I just want to wash away this experience.

I ask Shannon, "Will you watch the macaroni and cheese while I shower?"

"Yes, hurry up, I need to go get dressed." "Okay, thanks, I'll be right out."

Have you ever lost control of your emotions and a situation escalated out of control? Who brought the situation back to order? How did you reset? Was resolution restored or were things just left as they were? How long did it take to restore normalcy? What did you do? How do you handle things when the people who are supposed to love you don't? What do you do when you don't love the people that you're are supposed to love?

I step into the steaming hot shower, the water pitter-patters over my body. I've got to regroup. Cicely will not destroy Thanksgiving. Ah, I'll wash my hair, it helps me to clear my head and reset. It symbolically washes away the worries or frustrations that I encounter. It's just what I needed. After my shower, I am renewed. I put my clothes, hair, and make-up on and go to the front room. Shannon is listening to music and sipping on a cocktail. The macaroni and cheese is done and on top of the stove. It smells delicious. I want some, but I'll wait. "You look refreshed and relaxed." "I'm better, I needed that."

"Good I'm glad, don't let her destroy your Thanksgiving. The family really needs this, I am glad you are home, sissy!"

"Me, too."

"I'm going to get dressed, Kelly is picking his mother and Michelle up, so don't worry about them."

"What about your crew are they all coming?"

"Yes, I talked to them, not sure if Tony is going to make it, he said they baked a turkey. Trevor is going to stop by to get it and bring it. Ivey and her crew are coming by."

"OK, whoever is supposed to be here will be here, we're going to have a good time."

"That's right, I'll be back when I'm done."

"Okay, I'll see you when you get back, thanks for today sissy."

"Awe, it's all good, y'all will be alright." Shannon leaves, and I check on the ham, it's almost done. Cicely stays in her room.

Within a half hour, my house is full of guest. My sisters, nieces, nephews, cousins, great nieces, and nephews their friends and significant others are piled in my duplex. It has been years since I've seen some of them. Everyone brought their dish. My parents finally show up. I wondered what was taking them so long. Daddy walks into the dining room – and I get the answer to my question. He makes several trips to the car, Timmy and my nephew's help him. He brings in turkey, ham, dressing, giblet gravy, greens, green beans, mashed potatoes, cranberry sauce, peach cobbler, chocolate cake, coconut cake, sweet potato pies, cheesecake, and pecan pie. He literally cooked an entire meal and brought it to my house. I should have known that he wasn't going to rest and let us do the work.

"Daddy, are you serious, did you really cook your own entire meal?"

"I just want to make sure it is enough food for everyone."

"It's enough food for the neighborhood, I told you we had it daddy."

"Well, I'm sure it will not go to waste. Where's my baby?"

"She's in her room mad at me."

"What did you do to her?"

"Nothing, being mad at me is her normal state."
Daddy disappears down the hallway. I am sure he goes to
baby her, which is precisely what she wants.

Cicely is his favorite grandchild. He won't come out
and say it out loud, but it is an unspoken fact. He believes she
can do no wrong and she believes he can do no wrong. They
both are wrong. The house is full and bustling with multiple
conversations. There are four generations here. We awe over
my niece's baby twins. They are the first set since my
mother. We take pictures and embrace one another. There is
so much love in the house. Daddy comes out of the room
with Cicely following close behind. Everyone shows her
love. She matriculates into the crowd.

It's time to eat, Daddy says grace and we all pack into
the kitchen and dining room to fix our plates. We have so
much food, there are four turkeys, two hams and a wide
variety of sides, desserts, and drinks. We enjoy ourselves. We
talk, laugh, and take more pictures. We share stories, watch
TV and listen to music. The kids play both inside and outside.
Daddy wants to make it to Bingo, yes on Thanksgiving, so he
and mom leave. There is a constant flow of traffic, each time

the crowd thins out a new wave of people come in. Mostly everyone packs to-go plates before they leave. By early evening, all my family is gone, including my kids. I'm tired and ready to relax for the night. I guess Danny isn't going to make it. I sit down on the couch.

Knock, knock, knock.

It's Brittney and her nephew. Chasity and Brian bring a homemade cake, she knows I love her lemon pound cake. My friend Marla is in town and stops by – I haven't seen her in years. We all eat again, I lost count of how many times I've eaten today. We catch up, laugh and take pictures. We have a wonderful time. These are the times that I enjoy being back home around the people that I have long-lasting, loving relationships with. Life at this moment is good.

Knock, knock, knock. I answer the door.

"Hey Danny, come on in, glad you could make it." He steps in, hugs me and kisses me on the cheek.

"How are you, sorry I'm so late."

"I'm great, no worries, you're fine."

"Hey, ladies this is Danny. Danny, you know Chasity this is Brittney, and Marla is here from Dallas."

"Hello, ladies how are you all?"

"Fine." "Good." "Great, how are you?" The ladies all respond.

"I'm well." After a few moments of small talk, the ladies gather their belongings and prepare to leave.

"Don't leave on my account, I didn't mean to break up the party."

"Oh, you're not breaking up anything, we've been here a while, and I have a couple of more rounds to make."

"Oh, I've been going all day, I'm ready to go settle down."

"I need to get my nephew home to his parents. It was nice to meet you."

"Nice meeting you too ladies. Hopefully, I will see you all again."

We all say our goodbyes and the three of them leave out together. I close the door and turn to Danny.

"Glad you could make it. The house has been jammed packed all day. There were over forty people here throughout the day."

"Wow, you really know how to bring them out."

"Just glad to host. It's been a long time since I spent Thanksgiving in Tulsa."

"It's really good to see you again, do you want anything to eat?"

"Looks like you all had plenty of food."

"We did." I fix Danny a plate, and we talk while he eats.

"I really need to shower. Here's the remote to the television."

I retreat to my bedroom and get in the shower. I don't want to leave Danny alone too long, so I take a quick shower and change into something comfortable. I return to the living room, and to my surprise Danny has cleaned the kitchen.

"Oh, wow, you didn't have to do that. I'm grateful."

"No problem, I saw that everyone left you with all the clean-up, I don't mind helping."

He put everything away except a pot of greens.

"There isn't enough space for the greens, so I left them out."

"Oh, I will make room from them."

I open the refrigerator, shuffle food around and stack it differently until I maneuver enough room for the greens. I place the large pot in the refrigerator.

"See, I told you I could make room." "They would have been fine."

"I didn't want them to sit out all night." Danny's energy shifts. He stands erect, and his small lips are stiff.

"What's wrong?'

"Nothing." He grabs his coat off the back of the dining room chair. He's clearly agitated.

"Are you upset with me?" He sighs and puts on his coat. I am truly perplexed I don't know why he is upset with me.

"I'm going to head out, you have a good night." Oh-Kaaaaay, wow.

"You just got here." Then it dawns on me he's mad about the greens.

"Are you really upset with me because I put the greens away."

"I cleaned the kitchen, and your focus is on the one thing that I left out."

"I'm sorry I didn't mean to offend you. I was just making room for them."

"I'll talk to you later." He walks to the door. I stand at the door in amazement. Wow, this is why I have no interest in dating, little things become big things. I am home alone and relish in the peace and quiet. I go to bed and reflect on the day, though emotionally charged overall it was a good day.

After our Thanksgiving debacle, Cicely moves in with my parents. Daddy takes her back and forth to school every day. One week of her absence turns to two and so on. I am accustomed to her absence. However, Timmy isn't, he misses his sister and asks when she's coming back home. I don't have an answer for him. I focus on Timmy, school, and work. Danny and I see each other regularly. Today, he asks where Cicely is? Gone, that where she is. I am not telling him about our shit. If she decides she wants to get with the program, she can come back home. I decide not to allow Cicely's emotional outbreaks to control my actions. I want us to be under one roof, but until she gets it together, she is fine where she is.

Proud Peacock

Mom called last night to let me that Elle is back in the hospital and things are looking grim, the cancer has spread throughout her entire body. Elle is my mother's best friend since grade school. Elle is a free spirit. Her only child Gail is older than all seven of my mom's children.

Elle had the freedom to live life as she chose, and she did. I hated her as a child. I blamed her for my mother not loving me or caring for me like I thought she should have. Mom and Elle partied a lot. If they weren't partying at our house, they were in the clubs. My mother lived life as if she did not have children that needed to be raised at home. On any given day or night there were plenty of men, liquor, beer, cigarettes, marijuana, and pills floating about. There was a blatant disregard for us minors living in the house. I am the youngest of a combined ten children, my oldest sibling is fourteen years older, and the closest in age is five years older. Being the youngest, I felt like the "oops" child, like mom was done manufacturing babies and then I came along. Throughout my childhood, I misplaced my anger towards Elle, when the anger should have been placed at my mother. Somewhere around nineteen years old is when I accepted my mother for exactly who she is. As a thirty-nine-year-old full-grown woman, I lost my disdain for Elle, especially watching her in the hospital bed as she nears the end her of life. I take my mom to visit Elle in the nursing home and occasionally sit and visit with them.

I stop by St. John's hospital after church. I park the car and scurry across the parking lot. It's a blistery, chilly, windy day. I am thankful that my wig is safely secured. I enter the hospital corridor and see an attendant seated at the information desk. I ask her for Elle's room number.

She gives the number and directs me to the elevators. I thank her and walk off. I exit the elevator and stride towards Elle's room. The door is closed so I tap on it.

"Come in." I walk in. I expect to see Elle alone, however, she isn't. To my surprise, Gail is here. Mom didn't mention she was in town.

"Hey, Allison."

"Hey, Gail, it's been awhile." "Yes, it has."

"Hey, Elle," I say.

"Hey, Allison, good to see you," Elle responds.

"Mom told me you were in the hospital, so I stopped by after church."

"I'm glad you came," Elle said. Her sister Erma – who I haven't seen since I was a pre-teen, another middle-aged lady, and an older gentleman are also in the room. I speak to them.

Erma looks like she sees a ghost. She stands up and places her hand across her slightly opened mouth.

"Allison? Is, that you?" "Yes, it's me."

"Wow, you are beautiful, look at you. You look amazing."

I'm wearing a Tahari cream two-piece skirt set, adorned with big, bold jewelry and a cream Ann Taylor coat. My BCBG cream double strap, zipper back heels complete my outfit. Of course, my makeup is flawless, and the full ringlets of my black wig cascade down my face and halt midway down my back.

"Thank, you." I blush and smile like a proud peacock spreading its wings.

I am not prepared for what she says next, "I never understood, why your mother hated you so much."

She looks perplexed as if she is really attempting to comprehend like this question has plagued her for years. It takes me a moment to realize what she said. I am standing here in the middle of the hospital room of my mother's dying best friend. There are several people in the room, some of them strangers and her sister just said, she never understood why my mother hated me. I revert back to five years old; I hear my mother say.

"I hate you, you, little black motherfucker!" I hear the words so often that I think my name is little black mother fucker. I know without a hint of doubt that my

mother hates me, what I didn't know is that it is public information. I am mortified that it's common knowledge. My body stiffens, and I keep a straight face. Here I am a thirty-nine-year-old, grad school attending, Lexus-SUV driving, looking like I have it all together woman. I am the Director of Health Services. It's funny how my work title, degrees, or luxury vehicle can't protect me from this blow.

Nor can the designer clothes, flawless makeup and a lacefront wig soften the sucker punch. Not even the full armor of Christ protects my heart at this moment, I am a dressed up mess. The peacock feathers fall. Wow, what a reality check! When I mentally return to the room, she's still talking.

"Look at you now! You turned out better than the rest of them. She liked them better than she liked you."

"Do you live in Atlanta?" "No, I live here now."

"I believe she hated you because your daddy loved you. She would say, he spoils that girl! Anything she wants, he gives her, I can't stand her! You are so beautiful."

I am still in awe. I am wounded.

She is having this conversation as if she's talking about the weather, she is very calm, and strangely so is everyone else in the room, which makes this situation even more odd to me. It appears that everyone in the room,

including the people that I don't know, knows this fact about my mother and I's relationship. It feels like I am on stage with bright lights shining on me and all the people in the audience know my terrifying, life-crippling secret. My mother never loved me! I am uncomfortable, but I don't let it show. I've learned to mask anything that hurts me by looking unbothered, as if I don't have a care in the world. I finally muster "Well, you know my mother." That's it. I cannot physically utter any other words about it. My throat is closing in, I've lost my voice. I am light- headed. I am mentally and emotionally crushed, but I don't flinch. I switch the conversation back to Elle.

"How are you feeling today?" I ask Elle.

"Awe, Allison I am pretty good," she says as her eyes meet mine, I see in her eyes what she doesn't say. Her eyes say, I am better than you must feel right now. I am sorry that my sister is being so insensitive. I am sorry that your mother hated you and that she didn't hide it from anyone that would listen. Her eyes are empathetic to my inner chaos. For the first time in my life, I have compassion for Elle. I'd hated her for so long, but in this moment, I can only imagine what it must be like being my mother's best friend. I am sure she holds many of my mother's secrets, those much deeper than the fact that she hated me. I stay another fifteen minutes and then I leave the hospital.

My heart is heavy. I need to get this experience off my chest. I am hurt and angry with my mother. Feelings of my childhood insecurities creep in. I can't believe she told people outside of the home that she hated me. She never hid that fact from me, but I thought it was our secret. I remembered one time I was attempting to erase an old tape on an old school tape recorder. If you pressed play and record at the same time, you could delete or record over what was previously on the tape. It was hard to erase tapes because the recorder picked up every little sound. I placed the recorder under the bed, and I was laying on the floor next to it. Mom was enraged about something, and she was going off. She was screaming and cursing about God knows what, but the infamous 'I hate you, you little black motherfucker' was a part of the tirade. She went on for several minutes berating me and letting me know how

much she hated me. I wasn't trying to record her, but every word she uttered was recorded. I later listened to the recording and called my daddy who was in Alaska working at the time and played it for him. That didn't go over too well. He called to confront her. She denied it, and he told her he heard the recording. I got cursed out some more. She accused me of recording her on purpose. I attempted to

174

explain to her I was erasing a tape, but she was not trying to hear that.

Tears stream down my face and I head to Chasity's house. I need to vent and get this out. I am a wreck! I call Chasity to let her know that I am on my way and need to talk, she doesn't answer the phone. I call two more times and still no answer. I drive to her house anyway – this is an emergency, and I need an intervention. I pull into her driveway, look in the mirror, wipe my face and freshen my makeup. I knock on the door, Brian answers.

"Hey Ms. Allison."

"Hey Brian, is your mother home?" "Yes, she's here, she's in the kitchen." "Hey Ma, Allison's here."

I walk into the kitchen and Chasity is in the kitchen talking to her son Tristan. We all spoke.

"Hey Allie-Oop, what's up?" Chasity playfully says.

"I've been calling you," I reply.

"You have?"

"Yes, like three times."

"Oh, my phone is in the bedroom. Hey Ron, bring me my phone."

"I really need to talk to you." Ron emerges from the bedroom with Chasity's phone and hands it to her.

Ron and I exchange greetings.

"Oh shoot, you did call, I'm sorry my phone was on silent since church."

"I really need to talk to you."

"Chasity starts talking to Ron about what they're cooking for dinner as if she didn't hear me." They talk a few minutes.

"Chasity, I really need to talk to you."

She halfheartedly gives me her attention, but were constantly interrupted by Ron or the boys. I am an emotional wreck and Chasity can care less about what's bothering me. I finally have enough.

"Chasity, you're not listening, I've got to go." "Ok sorry, call me later," Chasity says.

I head out the door. I'm furious, I really need to talk, but Chasity acts like I'm bothering her. I get in my car and head home. I have a dull headache from the emotional roller coaster. Why is this still bothering me at thirty-nine years old? I thought I had released all this pain when I was nineteen. My thoughts are racing, and my head is spinning. I just need to be at home in bed to process. The pain of my childhood relationship with my mother still lingers. I am enraged, but I'm finally home. I press the garage door opener and pull in the garage and go straight to my room. Thank goodness Timothy isn't home. School is out for winter break, and Timothy is at my parents. I'm home alone. I didn't want him to see me like this. I can't shake my frustration with mom and Chasity. I have to get this out. I grab my journal and write.

How can someone give birth to you, but hate you and tells everyone? What did I do to deserve this?

I hate Tulsa, why did I ever move back here? I should have dealt with the embarrassment of going back to Atlanta. I write, cry, write some more, and cry some more until I drift off to sleep. I woke up around 9:30 p.m. The house is dark and still. I've missed a few calls and text messages. Chasity called and texted, but I'm over her right now. I don't want to talk to anyone. I fix a sandwich and prepare for bed. I've got to go to work tomorrow. The office is slow, mostly everyone is off for the holidays. Thursday please hurry up and get here. I look forward to the downtime for the next week.

Karma

It's Friday, oh yeah, I get to sleep in. Ring, ring, ring.

Who's calling me this early? It's not even eight o'clock yet.

"Hello."

"Hey Ma, I'm ready to come home. Please come get me. Timothy, what is going on?"

"Grandma is acting funny," he says. That typically means she is being mean and acting like she doesn't want them at the house.

"I'll be there as soon as I get dressed." I get out of bed and get myself together. I head to pick up Timothy. I am still perturbed with my mother and don't want to deal with any dumb mess. I arrive at my parent's house as I approach the door. I hear my mother fussing at Timothy and Cicely.

"I don't want to be bothered, I don't know why y'all's mother thinks I want to be bothered with y'all when she doesn't want to," I hear my mother say.

I walk in and under no uncertain terms let my mother have it. "You don't have to be bothered with them. My kids have a home to come to. They don't have to come over here ever again! I will not allow you to treat them the way you treat everyone else!"

"Timothy, Cicely go get yall's things, we're going home. "Far as I am concerned you don't ever have to see them again!"

"Daddy, if you want to see the kids or me, you'll have to come to my house to see them, and don't bring her with you!"

As usual, daddy just sits there looking like a sad puppy, he doesn't say a word.

"Y'all hurry up! I'll be in the car!" I go sit in the car and wait for the kids. When they get in the car, I pull off.

"What is she tripping about this morning?," I ask.

"She just woke up in a bad mood and started fussing about everything."

"Well, you all know how grandma is. I think she is upset about her friend that's sick," Timothy said.

"Well, that is no excuse to lash out at you all. Oh, well I am not in the mood for any drama today. Let's go get something to eat."

Cicely and I don't discuss her returning home, it is unspoken. It was time for her to come home, and I can tell by how quickly she packed her bags that she was ready! We spend the rest of the day together running errands and hanging out. We decide to have a family movie night and spend some quality time together. We need this, at least I do. We pick up a few Red Box movies. Once we get settled, I microwave two bags of popcorn and put the movie on. Five minutes into the movie, I fall asleep. I wake up just before it was over and somehow I'm on track with the storyline. I don't know how I do that.

It's early Christmas morning, and my phone is ringing early. I look at the phone, it's my parents. I assume its Daddy because I'm not speaking to Momma. To my surprise, it's Momma sobbing into the phone. "Elle died!

Gail found her in bed this morning. She is not sure what time she died, but it was after midnight. My friend is gone, all of my friends are dying."

"I'm sorry to hear that, I know Elle meant a lot to you, you all had a really long friendship."

"I love you, and I'm sorry for the other day with the kids, bye," Momma says.

She hung up the phone. Death sucks, every time someone dies it brings back the memories of the last person that died. I am not sure how to comfort my mother, I know she is hurting, but she is still wrong how she treats people. I see why I lived away for so long. When you live in an area that you don't have many ties to, death doesn't impact you like it does when it's the people that have been a part of your life for most of your life. It hurts especially on the holidays. Its Christmas now, and we spend part of the day at my parents and the remainder of the day at home. Danny stops by. We exchange gifts and watch a movie. I turn in a bit early as I am emotionally drained. I lay in bed and replay the past few weeks over and over in my head. Why did I come back here? I should have kept driving and gone back to Atlanta. I would have figured it out. I don't need to go down the rabbit hole of depression, so I go to sleep. Elle's funeral is somber. I don't particularly like going to funerals, but I go with my parents to support my mother. Elle's death is really taking a toll on her. She is the last one living of her siblings, and all of her friends are passing away. I can only imagine what that must feel like. We are no strangers to death as we've had our share of untimely deaths in our family, which is another reason I don't like living here. It is a constant reminder of the unsolved murders of my two brothers and two nephews. Lord, why? There must be a purpose for me being back here, I am just unclear to what that purpose is.

Since being back, working out and eating healthy have been my solid ground. I also went to the weight doctor, and the results are amazing. I'm feeling good, and looking good, so, at the last minute, I decide to attend the 20 Gents New Year's Eve Party at the Greenwood Cultural Center with Danny and some other friends. I am of course excited to find a dress for the occasion. I take the ten- minute drive to my favorite place – my escape from the world lay in the four walls of Name Brand Clothing. I pull in the parking lot and grab the first open space. Walking in the door, I turn my cell phone to vibrate. I spend the next three hours looking for the perfect dress for the party. I decided on a metallic silver, one shoulder, goddess mini dress with a black beaded attached belt. It has pockets and perfectly hugs my curves. I love the way it exposes my shoulders and my arms. My long arms are slender and muscular. I look like a chocolate Hersey's kiss wrapped in the metallic silver dress or more like a Black Roman Goddess. Perfect! I leave the store and go home to relax for a few hours. Danny picks me up at nine o'clock. Tulsa is easy to get around, we arrive to the party in twenty minutes.

My friend Toni meets me with our ticket and escorts us to our table. We take our coats off and wiggle our way to the dance floor. It's packed in here. A lot of people are home for the holidays. Danny and I dance to multiple songs and come back to the table. He gets us drinks and we eat. We're back on the dance floor – and at the stroke of midnight – we kiss.

"Happy New Year," we say simultaneously.

The way he touches the small of my back lets me know what I am in store for at the end of the night. We're in a room full of people, and it feels like we were the only ones here. We have this unspoken language that queues one another in on our sexual desires. We have amazing sexual chemistry, a glance or a touch and we both know a night of bliss is in store. Tonight, is no different. We say our goodbyes to our friends and leave the party.

While walking to the car Danny asks, "Your place or mine?"

"Yours is closer," I respond.

I can hardly wait to get to the house. I have been anticipating making love to Danny all night. The garage door barely shuts before we are all over each other.

Maxwell, his pitbull, greats us at the door. I stop to speak to him, Danny pulls me to the bedroom.

As soon as we enter the room, we passionately attack one another. His kisses – oh my – he is the perfect kisser, not too wet and not too dry. He is very intentional. His kisses are just hard enough to make my nipples stand at attention and to make me wetter than a waterfall. His teeth are perfectly straight with a sparkle that is nothing short of amazing.

He could easily be in a Colgate toothpaste commercial. His thin lips feel amazing on my skin. Oh, he is one handsome man! Tonight's ambiance makes him even finer. His 6'1 slender frame and caramel-butterscotch completion makes me hungry for him. His bald head glistens in the moonlight from his bedroom window. I am a sucker for bald-headed men. I lick his head from front to back and from ear to ear. His salt and pepper, immaculately sculpted beard frames his oval face. It is not to thick and burly and not to wiry and thin, it is perfect. I trace my fingers over the outline of his beard. The hairs feel soft and prickly against my fingers. Danny quickly undresses me and flings my dress and underwear across the room. He leaves my shoes on for now. I help him undress, damn… he is equipped with one of the largest packages I've ever had. The length, the width, the girth, oh my! I lose my breath each time he enters me.

The anticipation is getting to me. I want to feel him deep inside of me now, but I know that isn't about to happen. We never rush into sex. We spend at least forty minutes with foreplay each time we make love. I am ready for whatever he is offering tonight. I need him. I want him. I love him.

I am spread across his king-sized bed, and his eyes scope my nakedness. He approaches me cautiously, like a surgeon preparing to complete the most complicated surgery of his career. He studies my body. He knows what makes me tick. He loves the way I respond to his touches, kisses, licks, sucks and blows over my body. He enjoys how I quiver as he licks and tastes my clitoris. I love when he moans on it. The vibrations from his voice tingle me until I am in an orgasmic coma. He leans into me, I place my left shoe on his chest to stop him. The soft pain excites him.

I place my right shoe on his chest too. He spreads my legs and licks my leg from my ankle up while he unbuckles the strap on my shoe. He slightly nibbles on the inside of my leg. He alternates from leg to leg as he removes both shoes. He moves up to my thighs and continues this game. I am throbbing. I want him desperately– I crave him. I am anxious and ready to receive him. I've been waiting for this moment since I smelled his cologne. We have an incredible sexual chemistry. He knows what I like and provides it. I enjoy pleasing him. He is concentrating on my thighs and moves right past my sweet spot to my stomach, and then makes his way to my breasts. He treats them like prized possessions. He cups one and circles his tongue on the areola and nipple of the other. He glides his tongue down the center of my chest and does the same exercise on the right breast while he cups and fondles the left one. He moves his way up my neck where he plants soft kisses on it. His tongue glides across my lips and we kiss intently. Our passion is magnetic, I am so turned on.

He makes his way down to my vagina and spreads the walls of my labia with his middle and pointer fingers. He licks my labia as if he's licking his favorite ice cream. He licks and sucks my clitoris then sticks his tongue inside my vagina.

His tongue ravishes me. I am soaking wet. He licks me all over, and I love every moment of it. He hums on my clitoris and taps the top of my mons pubis. Within seconds I am squirting like a water hose. I scream in ecstasy as the orgasms come back-to-back. My screams excite Danny. He is focused on keeping me satisfied. I lose count of the orgasms I've had. My body shakes and convulses hard with each orgasm until I have the motherload of all orgasms. I feel it wailing up in my body like a ball of fire flowing, it starts in my toes and works its way up to my head and back down to the soul of my vagina. The eruptions feel like a tidal wave. I moan and scream at the top of my lungs. I sound like a wolf howling. I shake so hard it feels like I am having a seizure. I am sensitive to touch. Every time Danny touches me, I have another small orgasm. I attempt to get away from him, but he is locked in on me to ensure that he doesn't miss a drop of my nectar. My juices are flowing rapidly. I reach utopia with him.

Somewhere between my voyage to Neptune and Pluto, Danny enters me. I momentarily stop breathing. I resume breathing once he adjusts his well-endowed penis inside of me.

Oh, my, this man is gifted! I secretly thank God for him. I am still floating amongst the galaxies as I feel his forward thrust deeper inside me. My body responds accordingly and so does his. I return from my trip to the outer limits and gaze into his eyes. He looks deep into my eyes, peering into my soul. I stare at him intensely and shifted my body to receive more of him. He is an amazing lover. He adjusts himself slightly and presses his forearm on my neck. The slight pressure of the pseudo-choke excites me. He is the first person to choke me and I like it. I think I may be a freak and he loves it. I have at least seven more orgasms.

I am exhausted. The whole experience felt like heaven. In this moment, I think that perhaps I can get used to living in Tulsa. That's all I remember before we pass out.

Acknowledgements

I'd like to thank my creator for giving me the talent and courage to authentically write my story. I thank the universe for bringing the right people into my life during this journey. To my children and the relationships that we are now building, cultivating, and nurturing as we heal together. Also, for allowing me to expose you to the world. I love y'all to the galaxies and back.

To my friends who encouraged me to finish the book, allowing me to read chapters and providing much appreciated feedback. For those of you that ordered the book in 2017/2018 and didn't ask for your money back, I hope the story is worth your extended wait.

To my cousin Marla for encouraging me over the years and pressing print on the manuscript. To my editor Attiyya Atkins for your patience and exceptional ability to make my words pop while keeping the book in my voice. To the reader, thank you for having enough interest in my story to purchase my book. I appreciate your support, pass *A Dressed Up Mess* on to someone that needs to know that their chaos is a necessary part of their journey. Finally, I thank my husband David West, for believing in me, investing in me, and accepting me exactly as I am. I love you and am excited to share my life with you as we embark on our journey together.

Made in the USA
Columbia, SC
19 November 2019

83527096R00117